MycoMedicinals

*An Informational Treatise
on Mushrooms*

By Paul Stamets

Assisted by C. Dusty Wu Yao

This treatise was greatly aided by the able assistance of Carolyn Dusty Wu Yao who helped in literature searches and proofreading. Andrew Lenzer was instrumental in bringing this booklet into production. I want to acknowledge Andrew Weil for his continued support and Neal Mercado, Thomas Newmark, Regan Nally, Natalie Parks, Kevin Schoenacker, Paul Schulick, Solomon Wasser and *The International Journal of Medicinal Mushrooms*. Last but not least, are all the great people at Starship FP who have been instrumental in carrying the torch of medicinal mushrooms and to those kindred spirits who have helped to advance the cause of medicinal mushrooms.

ISBN: 0-9637971-9-0

MycoMedia® Productions, a division of Fungi Perfecti, LLC

P.O. Box 7634, Olympia, WA 98507 USA

Phone: (800) 780 9126   Fax: (360) 426 9377

Printed in China through Colorcraft Ltd., Hong Kong

MycoMedicinals® is a registered trademark of Paul Stamets.

Design and layout: Shukyo Lin Pfleger and Andrew Lenzer

This booklet is intended to be a resource guide on medicinal mushrooms. The compiled data will also be useful to physicians, naturopaths, acupuncturists, researchers, and end-users. This booklet is for educational and research purposes only. It is not intended to be a guide for self diagnosis or self medication. Medicinal mushrooms are not substitutes for professional medical care. You should consult a qualified health care practitioner familiar with your medical condition and history before using any of the mushrooms or recommendations in this book.

Front Cover: Aerial view of Skookum Inlet, Kamilche Point, Southern Puget Sound in Washington State, home of Fungi Perfecti, LLC

Table Of Contents

Introduction
Forest Fungi: Potent Allies for Medicine   5
Cross Index of Mushrooms and Therapeutic Effects   13
Key Reference Articles   14
Activities of Medicinal Mushrooms in the Treatment of Disease
Cross Specificity of Cancers and Mushrooms   17
Polypores: The Ancient Ones
Fomes fomentarius: Ice Man Fungus or Amadou   18
Fomitopsis officinalis: Agarikon   20
Ganoderma applanatum: Artist Conk   22
Ganoderma lucidum: Reishi or Ling Chi   24
Grifola frondosa: Maitake   29
Inonotus obliquus: Chaga   32
Phellinus linteus: Meshima   34
Piptoporus betulinus: Birch Polypore   36
Polyporus umbellatus: Zhu Ling   38
Schizophyllum commune: Split Gill Polypore or Suehirotake   40
Trametes versicolor: Turkey Tail or Yun Zhi   42
Teethed Fungi
Hericium erinaceus: Lion's Mane or Yamabushitake   45
Gilled Mushrooms
Agaricus blazei: Royal Sun Agaricus or Himematsutake   47
Flammulina velutipes: Enokitake   50
Lentinula edodes: Shiitake   51
Pleurotus ostreatus: Oyster   55
Insect Parasitizing Mushrooms
Cordyceps sinensis: Cordyceps or Dong Chong Xia Cao   57
Commonly Asked Questions   63
Bibliography
Supporting References   74
Noteworthy Popular Articles   92
Books on the Medicinal Properties of Mushrooms   92
*Journals & Notable Proceedings on the Medicinal
    Properties of Mushrooms*   92
Short Glossary   93
Index   94
Photo Credits and Other Books by the Author   96

Paul Stamets crouching beside *Bridgeoporus nobilissimus*, the first mushroom to be listed as an endangered species and a resident exclusive to the old growth rainforests of Washington and Oregon.

Introduction

Forest Fungi: Potent Allies for Medicine

"Fungi Perfecti, owned and operated by Paul
Stamets, is the best all-round source for
medicinal mushroom products and information."

—Dr. Andrew Weil,
in *Dr. Andrew Weil's Self Healing Newsletter,*
"Miraculous Mushrooms," May, 1997

Scientists have only recently confirmed what ancient cultures
have known for centuries: mushrooms have within them some of
the most potent medicines found in nature. Long viewed as tonics,
we now know that their cellular constituents can profoundly improve the quality of human health. Differing from most pharma-
ceuticals, these healing agents have extraordinarily low toxicity,
even at high doses. As fungi and animals share a more recent
common ancestry than with plants, protozoans and bacteria, fungal medicines are active against many diseases that afflict humans. A peculiarity of nature is that we suffer from many of the
disease organisms that afflict fungi, but in general, are not susceptible to those infecting plants. Many scientists believe this relationship occurs because we are more closely related to fungi
than to any other kingdom, having shared a common ancestor
more than 460 million years ago, and thus developed defenses
against mutual microbial enemies. For physicians, naturopaths,
herbalists, and lay people, medicinal mushrooms may well hold
answers for many of today's major health concerns. Increasingly,
medicinal mushrooms are valued not only as adjuvant therapies
to allopathic practices, but show promise for preventing diseases,
including cancer.

Medicinal mushrooms came to the forefront of western medical science largely through Dr. Ikekawa whose seminal epidemiological study compared the cancer rates in Nagano Prefecture

from 1972-1986. Working as a researcher for the National Cancer Institute of Japan, he found that the cancer death rates of families of Enoki mushroom growers were remarkably lower than the background population (Ikekawa, 1989). Upon studying 174,505 individuals, the cancer rates for men dropped from 160 per 100,000 to 58, and for women the improvement was from 70 per 100,000 to 40. This led to the discovery of proflamin, a water-soluble, orally active, low-molecular-weight polysaccharide useful for potentiating the immune system (Ikekawa, 2001). From this discovery and that of other researchers, primarily from Japan and China, research into the medicinal properties of mushrooms gained momentum and caught the attention of Western scientists.

In this treatise, I am describing 17 of the more important mushroom species. The more prominent species are wood conks or polypores. These include Reishi or Ling Zhi (*Ganoderma lucidum*), Maitake (*Grifola frondosa*), Meshima (*Phellinus linteus*), Zhu Ling (*Polyporus umbellatus*), and Yun Zhi (*Trametes versicolor*). Their underbellies have thousands of pores rather than the gills seen with the classically shaped Button mushroom, for example. Gilled mushrooms with notable medicinal properties include Shiitake (*Lentinula edodes*), Enokitake (*Flammulina velutipes*), Himematsutake (*Agaricus blazei*) and Oyster (*Pleurotus ostreatus*). Yet another group of mushrooms produces ball-shaped mushrooms with cascading icicle-like spines, including Yamabushitake or the Lion's Mane (*Hericium erinaceus*). Legendary for its medicinal properties, and heralding from the Himalayas, the last species is indeed bizarre: Dong Chong Xia Cao (*Cordyceps sinensis*)—a parasite on caterpillar larvae (*Lepidoptera* species)—and is used to enhance stamina, improve liver and kidney functions, and as an overall revitalizing tonic.

Most of these mushrooms and/or their close allies are widely distributed throughout the world. However, each strain is unique. For more than 20 years, I have sought out, purified and tested strains, paying particular attention to vigor, competitiveness, form and habitat. My best strains have originated from the pristine, virgin rainforests where I go frequently in pursuit of new candidates. Maintaining cell lines closest to their genetic origins ensures that the strains maintain their potency in being able to fully molecularize into exquisite forms. A mushroom is composed of compacted and/or differentiated mycelium, the same thread-like chains of cells seen beneath a mushroom when you pick one. The transformation of the mycelium into a mushroom is magical. To those skilled in the art, this ability of the mycelium to form a mushroom, a sophisticated structure from a seemingly undifferentiated mycelial mass, is the life force pathway that also gives

6

Fomitopsis officinalis was viewed as a powerful medicinal mushroom, used by North Coast shamans to treat diseases that originated from the 'spirit' world. This mushroom was also central to the origination myth of Haida women. Known to the Greeks as Agarikon, Dioscorides first mentioned this mushroom in approximately 65 C.E. in the treatment of coughing illnesses, including consumption, later to be known as tuberculosis. A perennial polypore, the specimen featured, (right) resembles the Venus of Willendorf form, the archetypal woman. The specimen featured below is approximately 40 yrs. old, judging by the annual growth rings. This mushroom inhabits the Old Growth forests of western Washington State, USA.

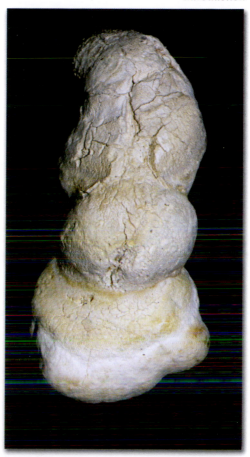

rise to many of the medically significant compounds. As nature is the mother of all strains, preserving the biodiversity of fungi in the natural environment is integral to our survival. In essence, fungi are central to the host defense of the planet and its people.

Mushrooms produce several notable medicinal compounds that are listed in the descriptions of the following 17 species. These compounds may be produced by either the mycelium—the fine wooly-web of cells giving rise to mushrooms and/or the *fruitbodies*—what we commonly call mushrooms. Notably the polysaccharides, high-molecular-weight sugar polymers, have attracted the most interest by researchers. The cell walls of mushrooms are generally tough, due to their polysaccharide content. Diverse sets of polysaccharides occur in mushrooms and their mycelia, many of which are biologically active when preheated or extracted before consumption. For instance, 28 unique polysaccharides have been isolated from the mycelium of Maitake, *Grifola frondosa*, while 29 have been isolated from the fruitbodies (Reshetnikov et al. 2001). Ikekawa (2001) noted that antitumor activity from water soluble polysaccharides of 'hard' mushrooms —the tough polypores like Reishi, *Ganoderma lucidum* and Yun Zhi, *Trametes versicolor*—are not as orally active when compared to the 'soft' edible medicinal mushrooms with cancers such as sarcoma and Ehrlich's carcinoma. However, mycelially derived products from these same mushrooms elicit a positive host-mediated response (Ghoneum 1994, 1995, 1998; Song et al, 1995; Matsushita et al. 1998). Compounds other than polysaccharides, such as triterpenoids, isolated from the Reishi mushroom, show strong immunomodulatory activity (Wang et al., 1997; Gao et al. 2002; Ooi et al. 2002). Although some studies show target-specificity with a mushroom constituent to a type of cancer, interactions with the immune system are complex. As research progresses, the best combinations of mushrooms for different cancers will be better understood.

The medicinally active compounds in mushrooms are primarily polysaccharides, glycoproteins, ergosterols, triterpenes and antibiotics. Polysaccharides that have drawn the most attention for their immune-enhancing and/or tumor-retarding properties are cell wall beta-glucans. In particular, the orally active, protein-bound polysaccharides, and polysaccharide derivatives can be viewed as precursor-nutrients, awakening the immune system, activating macrophages and gene expression of cytokines (Ooi & Lieu, 2000; Mondoa, 2001). Polysaccharide complexes are partially broken down by the action of acids and enzymes in the digestive system, and if heated before ingestion, they become more bio-available. Although all mushrooms have these cell wall sugars, several species have higher levels of polysaccharides effective in fighting cancer and other diseases. Additionally, arabinoxylanes derived from the conversion of rice bran by the mycelium's extracellular enzymes show enhanced immune response—comparative to those obtained from the beta glucan rich extracts from the fruitbodies of the same mushroom species. A common theme arising from the most recent studies underscores that mixtures of complex constituents from a score of mushroom species results in profound immunopotentiation. Research results from comparing 7 mushroom species in combination showed a greater effect in activating NK (natural killer) and macrophage responses than from any one species at the same dose (Ohtomo, 2002). Natural antibiotics produced by fungi can also limit the proliferation of bacteria, viruses and protozoans. Immunology is strengthened from at least six sources of diverse constituent families from fungi.

The first clinical trials in the United States by Ghoneum et al. (1994, 1995 & 1998) with cancer patients showed a multifold enhancement of natural killer (NK) cell activity and corresponding reduction in cancer markers and increased survival rates. As research progresses, we now know that a multitude of cellular constituents are medically significant in potentiating our host defenses. Metabolites from mushroom mycelium can remotely be antimicrobial (Anke, 1989). Extracellular, primary and secondary metabolites secreted from the exoskeleton of the mycelium produce natural antibiotics that can stave off or cure infection. In a recent study by Suay et al., (2000) 45% of 2 0 4 gilled and polypore species were active in inhibiting growth of microbes *in vitro*. Polypore mushrooms, as a group, showed stronger antimicrobial activity than gilled mushroom species surveyed. A higher percentage— 75% of the polypores tested—were antimicrobial. More anti-fungal antibiotics were found in gilled mushrooms than polypores. Turkey Tail, known as Yun Zhi to the Chinese (*Trametes* (*Coriolus*) *versicolor*) inhibits the growth of yeasts *Candida albicans* (Tsukagoshi et al., 1984; Sakagami et al., 1991) as does *Hericium erinaceus* (Kawagishi, 1994) and *Ganoderma lucidum* (Oh et al., 1998). Some anti-tumor polysaccharides from mushrooms inhibit bacteria (*Bacillus subtilis, Staphylococcus aureus, Escherichia coli, Pseudomonas aeruginosa*) directly as a toxin and indirectly through a host-mediated response. Additionally, mushroom mycelia can consume bacteria upon contact (Stamets 2002; Thomas et al. 1999). Lentinan from shiitake mushrooms, *Lentinula edodes*, is effective in retarding *Mycobacterium tuberculosis* and *Listeria monocytogenes* (Chihara, 1992). Cell-free water extracts of Shiitake mushroom mycelium demonstrate bacteriostatic activity against *Streptococcus pyogenes, Staphylococcus aureus* and *Bacillus megaterium* (Hatvani, 2001). *Polyporus umbellatus*, Zhu Ling, inhibits plasmodial parasites like the one causing malaria, *Plasmodium falciparum* (Lovy et al., 1999). The fact that mushrooms can treat our microbial diseases, and not harm human hosts, underscores their broad range of utility for ancient and modern medical practitioners.

The more prominent medicinal mushrooms are described herein. Most of these species are discussed in my book *Growing Gourmet & Medicinal Mushrooms* (2000, 3rd ed., Ten Speed Press, Berkeley). A great resource delving into the biochemistry of the medicinal properties is *Mushrooms: The Versatile Fungus-Food and Medicinal Properties* in *Food Reviews International* vol. 11, no.1. edited by Dr. Takashi Mizuno (1995, Marcel Dekker, Inc., New York). A recent book, *Sugars that Heal: The New Healing Science of Glyconutrients* by Dr. Emil Mondoa & Mindy Kiteii (Ballantine Books, New York) explains, in lay person's terms, the role of these unique sugars for improving immunity. A good summary of the anti-viral properties of mushrooms can be found in an article published by Curtis. B. Brandt and Frank Piraino, entitled *Mushroom Antivirals* in *Recent Research Developments* in *Antimicrobial Agents and Chemotherapies* 4 (2000): 11-26. Ooi and Liu (1999) give a good overview of the pharmacological activities of mushroom polysaccharides in the *International Journal of Medicinal Mushrooms* as does Wasser & Weis (1999). Accompanying this document is an extensive bibliography and list of other publications helpful in understanding the medicinal properties of mushrooms.

Polypores: the Ancient Ones

Polypore mushrooms are shelf or hoof-shaped, with pores underneath instead of gills, and are typically attached to trees or their roots. Amazingly, all polypores—so far as we know—are edible, that is, if you can consume them. They are typically tough in texture, even wood-like. To render the constituents bio-available, they, like all mushrooms, must be tenderized, typically through heating. Mycologists now believe that many gilled mushrooms evolved from polypores; the pores elongated over time, stretching out to form gills. In some cases polypores have re-evolved into gilled mushrooms. The evolutionary co-factors for steering this course of morphological development is not yet clear. Polypores as a group are comparatively benign compared to their gilled cousins, some of which can be very poisonous. Since time immemorial, polypores have been the ancient guardians of the forest and forest-peoples. They deserve our respect as allies for human survival.

Paul Stamets standing at the base of a Noble Fir harboring *Bridgeoporus (Oxyporus) nobilissimus*, The Noble Polypore.

Shamans have traditionally viewed polypores as powerful medicines. Conk-like mushrooms such as *Piptoporus betulinus*, the Birch Polypore, have been used medicinally for centuries. This mushroom was associated with Otzi, the 5300-year-old Ice Man who was discovered in the fall of 1991 on the border of Austria and Italy. Experts suspect that he used the Birch Polypore to help retard and purge metazoans and mycobacteria from his digestive system (Capasso et al., 1998). He also packed a specimen of *Fomes fomentarius*, the Tinder fungus, tethered to his right side. These mushrooms may have been essential for his survival and for his trek over the Alps. When dried, these hoof-shaped mushrooms are excellent as punk for starting fires and keeping embers alive, allowing travel over long distances. For our nomadic ancestors, the transportability of fire literally meant the difference between life and death. Polypores were also burned ritualistically, with the fragrant smoke being exceptional at repelling biting insects. When this conk is soaked and pounded into a pulp, a wooly mass is created which can be woven into garments, a tradition still surviving in Transylvania and surrounding regions. Having so many uses, it is no wonder that mushrooms were viewed as sacraments by prehistoric peoples.

Early on, indigenous peoples discovered that polypores are exceptionally good at preventing and curing infection. The Birch Polypore, *Piptoporus betulinus*, and the Ice Man Fungus, *Fomes fomentarius*, have strong antibacterial properties, effective externally and internally. Although most polypores are generally too tough to eat, native peoples long ago discovered that when boiled, a rich tea with health strengthening effects and antimicrobial properties could be made. Whether or not our ancestors understood

A hat and fabric made from *F. fomentarius*.

that many diseases were caused by microbes, the use of mushrooms by shamans to treat the spirit world shares in common the practice by doctors today to treat the microscopic, or the 'unseen universe' with a pantheon of antibiotic medicines (Stamets, 2002). For centuries, polypores have been used for making into poultices to treat cuts. These same antibiotics make mushrooms rot-resistant.

The reputation for their medicinal properties has largely been folkloric—until recently. We are just beginning to explore the many health benefits from mushrooms. They have within them a treasure trove of novel medicines. Research papers authenticating their benefits are being published with increasing frequency. Hundreds of research articles are cited here. This treatise is being continually updated as the knowledge base expands. Join us in this new revolution in integrative medicine using mushrooms as keystone components in preventative medicine and adjuvant therapies.

Cross Index of Mushrooms
and Targeted Therapeutic Effects

Therapeutic Effect	Agaricus blazei (Himematsutake)	Cordyceps sinensis (Cordyceps)	Flammulina velutipes (Enokitake)	Fomes fomentarius (Ice Man Polypore)	Ganoderma applanatum (Artist Conk)	Ganoderma lucidum (Reishi/Ling Chi)	Ganoderma oregonense (Oregon Polypore)	Grifola frondosa (Maitake/Hen of the Woods)	Hericium erinaceus (Yamabushitake/Lion's Mane)	Inonotus obliquus (Chaga)	Lentinula edodes (Shiitake/Xiang Gu)	Phellinus linteus (Mesima)	Pleurotus ostreatus (Hiratake/Pearl Oyster)	Polyporus sulphureus (Chicken of the Woods)	Polyporus umbellatus (Zhu Ling)	Schizophyllum commune (Suehirotake/Split-Gill)	Trametes versicolor (Yun Zhi/Turkey Tail)
stress reducer		•				•		•				•					
sexual potentiator		•										•					
nerve tonic		•				•	•							•			
lungs/respiratory		•			•	•	•	•							•		
liver tonic		•				•						•				•	•
kidney tonic	•	•	•			•	•	•	•	•		•			•		•
immune enhancer	•	•	•			•		•				•		•	•	•	
cholesterol reducer		•				•	•						•				
cardio-vascular	•	•				•		•			•		•				
blood sugar moderator		•				•		•					•				
blood pressure	•	•		•		•		•			•		•		•	•	•
anti-viral		•			•	•	•		•		•		•				
anti-tumor		•				•											
anti-oxidant				•	•	•			•				•	•		•	
anti-inflammatory						•					•						
anti-candida						•									•		
anti-bacterial	•	•	•	•	•	•	•	•	•	•	•	•	•	•	•	•	•

13

Key Reference Articles

Activities of Medicinal Mushrooms
in the Treatment of Disease

Some notable scientific articles are summarized here. For more information, see the descriptions for each individual species, and the cited bibliographic references.

Anti-arthritic/anti-inflammatory activity: Reishi derivatives compare favorably with Prednisone® but without negative side effects. (Stavinoha et al., 1990, 1996; Stavinoha, 1997). This and other mushrooms lessen inflammation (Ukai et al. 1983; Hobbs, 1995; Lin et al., 1993; Mizuno, 1995; Turner et al., 1980; Ooi & Liu, 1999; Small et al., 2000; Lee et al., 2001).

Anti-cancer activity: Anti-cancer activity: Numerous agents from a score of mushrooms retard cancer, primarily as biological response modifiers, activating systemic immune responses. (Ikekawa, 1969, 1989, 2001; Cochran 1978, Jong & Birmingham, 1992, Farnsworth et al., 1995; Mizuno, 1995; Volz, 1999; Ooi & Liu, 1999; Wasser & Weis, 1999; Kidd, 2000; Ooi & Liu, 2000; Reshetnikov, 2001; Zhou & Gao, 2002; Koh et al., 2002; Kawakami et al 2002). Clinical studies: Fujimoto et al.1984; Arika et al., 1986, Inomata et al., 1990; Hasegawa et al. 1990; Fujimoto et al. 1991; Miyazaki et al., 1995; Kimura et al., 1994; Nakazato et al., 1994; Yang et al. 1994; Zhou & Lin, 1995; Sugimachi et al., 1997; and Ghoneum et al. 1994, 1995, 1996 & 1998. Inhibition of enzymes such as aromatase, which is associated with the growth of breast cancer, has also been reported (Bankhead, 1999; Atsumi et al., 1990).

Anti-cholesterol activity: Anti-cholesterol effects reported from *Cordyceps sinensis* mycelia (Yamaguchi et al., 2000; Li et al., 2001), from *Pleurotus ostreatus* mushrooms (Gunde-Cimerman et al., 1995, 1998 and Bobek et al., 1998, 1999) from *Grifola frondosa, Lentinula edodes* and *Flammulina velutipes* (Fukushima et al., 2001). Reishi inhibits platelet aggregation and may be useful at preventing arteriosclerosis (Tao & Feng, 1990; Gau et al. 1990).

14

Anti-diabetic activity: Maitake (*Grifola frondosa*) and Reishi (*Ganoderma lucidum*) improve glucose tolerance in diabetic rats and is being explored as a treatment for controlling diabetes (Tomoda et al., 1986; Horio et al., 2001; Ohtsuru et al., 2001; Kubo et al., 1994; Konno et al., 2001; Manohar et al., 2002.)

Anti-fatiguing activity: Cordyceps (*Cordyceps sinensis*) increases endurance (Dai et al. 2001; Hiyoshi et al., 1996; Steinkraus & Whitfield, 1994) as does Reishi (*Ganoderma lucidum*) (Andreacchi et al., 1997; Yang & Wang 1994; Aoki et al., 1987; Chang & But, 1986). Both have been suggested to treat Chronic Fatigue Syndrome.

Anti-fibriotic activity: Reishi (*Ganoderma lucidum*) is being explored as an anti-fibriotic agent with some promising, but not definitive results. (Park et al., 1997).

Anti-microbial activity: Mushrooms have drawn the attention of scientists looking for primary and secondary metabolites effective against microbes: bacteria, protozoa and fungi. (Anke, 1989; Okamato et al., 1993; Ng et al., 1996; Sudirman, 1999; Thomas et al., 1999; Hirasawa et al., 1999; Hatvani, 2001; Trutneva et al., 2001; Suay et al., 2000; Stamets, 2002)

Anti-oxidative effects: Triterpene fractions and water-soluble compounds from *Ganoderma lucidum* show strong antioxidant properties. (Lin et al., 1995; Zhu et al., 1999; Kim et al., 2000; Li et al., 2000; Shi et al. 2002). Water extracts of *Cordyceps sinensis* also show similar antioxidant effects. (Li et al., 2001, 2002). Numerous studies have been published to date on the free radical scavenging ability of mushroom derivatives.

Anti-viral activity: Extracts of the Gypsy Mushroom, *Rozites caperata*, inhibit Herpes Simplex I & II (Piraino & Brandt, 2000). An ubiquitin-like substance from Oyster mushrooms, *Pleurotus ostreatus*, inhibits HIV (Wang & Ng, 2000), as do the water-solubized lignins from Shiitake mushrooms, *Lentinula edodes*. (Suzuki et al., 1990). Reports by Eo et al. (2000) and Kim et al. (1999) showed that water soluble fractions of Reishi contained potent antiviral properties against herpes simplex I & II, influenza A virus, and vesicular stomatitis virus while having a low cytotoxicity to the host. Mizuno et al. (1996) and Kahlos (1996) observed antiviral activity from water extracts of *Inonotus obliquus*. Arabinoxylanes inhibit HIV indirectly through the enhancement of NK cells which target the virus. Arabinoxylanes are created from mushroom mycelia's enzymatic conversion of rice bran (Ghoneum, M., 1998). Reishi, *Ganoderma lucidum*, has a hepatoprotective effect from the inhibition of liver-damaging beta-glucuronidases (Kim et al., 1999). Chaga, *Inonotus obliquus*, has unique antiviral agents (Kahlos et al., 1996). Numerous other mushrooms are being explored and have shown promising results against a wide variety of viral agents (Stamets, 2001a; Eo et al. 1999; Anke, 1999; Gordon et al., 1998). A good summary of the anti-viral properties of mushrooms can be found in Brandt & Piraino (2000). Clinical studies: Xiong (1993) and Yan (1988) successfully treated patients with chronic hepatitis B using *Polyporus umbellatus*. In a double blind study, Lin, Y. et al., 1987 noted that derivatives of Shiitake helped reduce counts of viral hepatitis and Zhou et al., 1990 had a similar result with the use of *Cordyceps sinensis*.

Chemo-protective & radio-protective activity: Several mushroom species have shown activity in reducing the negative effects of chemo- and radiation therapies, protecting healthy cells, and significantly helping the immune system rebound post treatment. Reishi (*Ganoderma lucidum*) Kim & Kim (1999), Zhu Ling (*Polyporus umbellatus*) Chang & But 1986, Turkey Tail, (*Trametes versicolor*) (Lin et al., 1996; Hayakawa et al., 1993; Chen et al., 1995); Suehirotake (*Schizophyllum commune*) Arika et al., 1986; Inomata et al., 1990; Hasegawa et al., 1990; Fujimoto et al., 1984 & 1991; Miyazaki et al. 1995). Clinical studies: Nakazato et al., 1994; Sugimachi et al., 1994; and Iino et al., 1995.

Mushrooms with Activity against Specific Cancers

The associated beneficial effects of mushroom species as supported by published studies.

Breast: *Grifola frondosa, Lentinula edodes, Trametes versicolor*

Cervical/Uterine: *Agaricus blazei, Inonotus obliquus, Inonotus obliquus, Phellinus linteus Schizophyllum commune, Trametes versicolor*

Colorectal: *Agaricus blazei, Grifola frondosa, Phellinus linteus*

Gastric/Stomach: *Hericium erinaceus, Phellinus linteus, Schizophyllum commune, Trametes versicolor*

Leukemia: *Cordyceps sinensis, Ganoderma lucidum Grifola frondosa, Polyporus umbellatus, Trametes versicolor*

Liver: *Ganoderma lucidum Grifola frondosa, Lentinula edodes, Phellinus linteus, Polyporus umbellatus, Trametes versicolor*

Lung: *Cordyceps sinensis, Ganoderma lucidum, Grifola frondosa, Polyporus umbellatus, Trametes versicolor*

Lymphoma: *Cordyceps sinensis, Flammulina velutipes*

Melanoma: *Lentinula edodes, Phellinus linteus, Piptoporus betulinus*

Prostate: *Flammulina velutipes, ,Ganoderma lucidum, Grifola frondosa, Lentinula edodes, Trametes versicolor*

Sarcoma: *Agaricus blazei, Ganoderma lucidum, Pleurotus ostreatus*

Medicinal Mushrooms

POLYPORES

Fomes fomentarius (L.:Fr.) J. Kickx

= *Polyporus fomentarius* L.:Fr.

Common Names
Amadou, Tinder Conk, Ice Man Polypore, Hoof Fungus, Hoof Conk, Tsuriganetabe

Distribution and Natural Habitat
Widespread throughout the boreal woodlands of the world —northern North America, Europe and the temperate birch and alder forests of the world, on dead and living trees.

Known Active Constituents
Polysaccharides
BAS (Basidiomycete Active Substance)
Extracellular antimicrobial metabolites
Glucose oxidase enzymes

Form Used
Conk
Mycelium on grain
Fermented mycelium

Medicinal Properties
Anti-tumor polysaccharides from the mycelium were isolated and tested by Ito et al. (1976). Novel ergosterol peroxides have been isolated from this fungus. (Rosecke et al., 2000). Water extracts of *F. fomentarius* have strong antiviral properties Aoki et al., 1993; Piraino & Brandt, 1999) and effectively inhibit the reproduction of *Bacillus subtilis* (Suay et al. 2000) and possibly many other species of Bacillus and bacteria (Hilborn, 1942). Vole et al. (1985) examined 40 species of fungi and found *F. fomentarius* and *Trametes versicolor* to have the

highest enzyme activity of converting D-glucose into dicarbonyl sugars, important considerations for fermentation manufacturing. Traditionally used as a styptic to stop bleeding and prevent infection, this mushroom is yet to be fully explored for its medicinal properties.

Comments

The Okanagan-Colville Indians of British Columbia and Washington traditionally used this mushroom to treat arthritis (Turner et al., 1980). The fruitbodies are woody and too tough to eat. The mushrooms can be boiled in water and an antimicrobial, immune-boosting water-extract or tea can be made. Mushrooms can be dried, cooked, and pounded into a powder and used as a poultice to stifle infection and help alleviate pain from swollen joints. With the invention of tissue culture, the mycelial form can be grown *en masse*, offering several options for medicinal use. Mycelium grown on grains allow for a form, when dehydrated and heat-treated, are digestible and bio-available.

A mushroom of many uses, this mushroom is a prominent species in the temperate forests of the world, being particularly fond of birch trees, although other trees, including firs, can be the host. The mycelium is multi-purposeful. The fruitbodies can be moistened and then pounded until the fibers separate into a wooly fabric-like mass. At Stone Age sites, remnants of this mushroom have been found, dating back to 11,600 BP, being the oldest known manipulated natural, i.e. biological, product discovered thus far. The first written record on *F. fomentarius* was from Hippocrates (2460-2377 BP) who mentioned its topical use for cauterizing wounds and for treating externally the outside of inflamed organs. The famous Ice Man or Otzi, found on the slopes of the Alps in 1991 on the border of Italy and Austria, had *F. fomentarius* 'wool' with him as well as whole fruitbodies. This wooly mass is dissociated mycelium (Stamets, 2002, pg. 33), and feels like felt—which some know as "German Felt." From China to Europe, this mushroom has had practical applications. Peintner et. al. (1998) list the following traditional uses: cauterization of wounds, styptic to stop bleeding; treatment for bladder infections; treatment for esophagus, stomach and uterine cancer; smoking as incense and with tobacco; making of clothing and hats. For the past few centuries, fishermen have used Amadou felt for keeping fishing flies dry.

The wooly mass is highly flammable, and was used as punk during the Middle Ages, resulting in a flourishing trade, as gunpowder-fired weapons became widespread. The punk made from this conk was essential for making flintlock guns function, allowing the spark from the flint to light the mycelium which, in turn, ignited the gunpowder. That a mushroom would help revolutionize warfare is another peculiar twist in the interactions of fungi and humans.

Fomitopsis officinalis (Villars) Bondarzew & Singer

= *Agaricum officinalis* Villars.: F.
= *Fomes officinalis*
   (Villars.:Fr.) Faull.
= *Fomes laricis* (Jac.) Murril
= *Laricifomes officinalis*
   (Villars.: Fr.) Kotlaba & Pouzar

Common Names
Agarikon, Quinine Conk, Larch Bracket Mushroom, Brown Trunk Rot, Eburiko, Adagan ('ghost bread'), Tak'a di ('tree biscuit')

Distribution and Natural Habitat
Once widespread throughout the temperate regions of the world, this perennial wood conk saprophytizes larch, Douglas fir, hemlock, preferring mature woodlands. Now nearly extinct in Europe and Asia, this mushroom is a resident of the Old Growth forests of Oregon, Washington and British Columbia.

Known Active Constituents
Beta glucans
Triterpenoids
Agaricin
Extracellular antibiotics

Form Used
Fruitbodies
Mycelium

Medicinal Properties

Antimicrobial, traditionally used for centuries for the treatment of tuberculosis and/or pneumonia, the primary causal organisms being *Mycobacterium tuberculosis*, *Bacillus pneumoniae* and/or other microorganisms. Mizuno et al. (1995a) and Hanssen (1996) include this mushroom in a group of polypores, the hot water extract of which provide a strong host mediated response. Agarikon was also applied topically, in a poultice, as an anti-inflammatory and to treat muscle/skeletal pain.

Comments

Described by the first century Greek physician Dioscorides in *Materia Medica*, the first encyclopedic pharmacopoeia on the medicinal use of plants, in approximately 65 C.E., as a treatment for a wide range of illnesses, most notably consumption, later known as tuberculosis. A resident on the Old growth conifers, especially spruce, hemlock, Douglas fir, and Larch, this amazing mushroom produces a chalky cylindrical fruitbody that adds layers of spore-producing pores with each growth season, allowing for a rough calculation of age. Conks up to 50 years have been collected, and often times they resemble a woman, reminiscent of the Venus of Willendorf form. The Haida First Peoples of the Queen Charlotte Islands, and elsewhere on the coast of British Columbia, associated this mushroom with the powerful creator spirit Raven, and as a protector of women's sexuality (Blanchette et al., 1992; Stamets, 2002). This mushroom was carved into animalistic forms and placed on shamans' graves to protect them from evil spirits. It is thought, but not yet proven, to have provided an aid in preventing the scourge of viral diseases such as smallpox, especially associated with the influx of Europeans into northwestern North America, which devastated the native populations. Grzywnowicz (2001) described the traditional use of this mushroom by Polish peoples, as a treatment against coughing illnesses, asthma, rheumatoid arthritis, bleeding, infected wounds, and was known for centuries as an *"elixirium ad longam vitam"*: elixir of long life.

The North Coast First Peoples of Northwestern North America also discovered the use of this mushroom as a poultice to relieve swellings and in teas for treating feverish illnesses. This mushroom is central to the origination myth of women by the Haida and other coastal tribes. Raven or Yaahl, the all-powerful spirit being, after seeking help from other creatures of forest and sea, finally found 'Fungus Man,' *Fomitopsis officinalis*, as the steerman for the canoe leading to the discovery of genitalia, completing the creation of women (Blanchette et al., 1992). From ancient Greece to the remote Queen Charlotte Islands of British Columbia, native peoples have independently discovered the medicinal value of this mushroom to treat diseases caused by the 'spirits.' The ethnobotanical evidence underscores that this mushroom may have played a critical role in the survival of pre-modern humans from infectious disease.

Called the Quinine Fungus in many forestry manuals because of its bitter taste, this mushroom is not the source of quinine, an alkaloid from the bark of the Amazonian *Cinchona ledgeriana* tree which was widely used since the late 19th century to treat malaria, caused by *Plasmodium falciparum*. Another polypore, *Polyporus umbellatus*, has shown activity against the malarial parasite (Lovy et al., 1999). This author is not aware of any trials testing *F. officinalis* against malaria.

Despite the long history of use, few modern studies have been published on its medicinally active compounds. *F. officinalis* merits further research as the number of strains is in rapid decline, especially in Europe, where it is on the verge of extinction (Leck, 1991). If our ancestors were correct, I suspect this species has yet to yield many discoveries of medical import—especially antimicrobial, antitumor and immunomodulating agents. As its mycelia can now be grown on grain-carriers and in fermentation, industrial production of mycomass in a form digestible to humans, or as a base for further fractionation, is now possible.

Ganoderma applanatum   (Pers. ex Wallr.) Pat.

= *Polyporus applanatus* (Pers.) Wallr.

Common Names
Artist Conk, Shelf Fungus, Tree tongue, White Mottled Rot Mushroom, Kofukisanunokoshikake, Kofukitake

Distribution and Natural Habitat
A perennial mushroom, widely distributed across the woodlands of the temperate and sub-tropics, growing on many hardwood tree species, but also on conifers, especially old growth Douglas firs in the Pacific Northwest of North America.

Known Active Constituents
ß-Glucans, hetero-ß-glucans
Ganoderic acids—triterpenes
Lanostanic triterpenoids
Antibiotics

Form Used
Fruiting bodies
Mycelia grown on grain

Medicinal Properties
Sasaki et al. (1971), along with the pioneering mycomedicinalist Ikekawa (1969) first studied *G. applanatum* for its anti-tumor properties. Protiva et al. (1980), Tokuyama et al. (1991), and Chairul (1994) identified triterpenes and steroids from *Ganoderma applanatum*. Smania et al. (1999) found that a methanol extract of *G. applanatum* fruitbody, further fractionated with hexane and ethyl acetate, showed significant activity against a wide range of bacteria, including *E. coli* and *Staphylococcus aureus*. Antimicrobial activity from mushrooms against *Escherichia coli* has been the subject of recent studies (Thomas et al., 1999; Suay et al., 2000; Stamets, 2002;).

Comments
A widespread and often mammoth species known and used for millennia, this mushroom has many attributes useful to our Paleolithic ancestors, and their descendents. *Ganoderma applanatum* is a perennial polypore, and can live for 40-50 years, perhaps longer. Producing a large, lateral shelf, flat in profile, the spores fall from the pores on the underbelly of the conk and due to electrostatic and thermal differentials, many of the spores float to settle on the top of the cap, dusting the upper-surface brown. The dried conk can be burned emitting a pleasant and insect-repelling smoke. When chunks are boiled for several hours, an amber looking, bitter tea is made. The tea can have diuretic effects and is strongly antimicrobial (Suay et al., 2001) showing potential as a purgatory of intestinal parasites and a treatment for bacterial diseases.

Often the mantle for artists, the large conks of *Ganoderma applanatum* have whitish pores that stain brown when bruised, allowing for etching. I have seen huge specimens, beautifully scored, depicting pastoral and sylvan scenes, and enthroned as the centerpiece in the living room of the owner. That this mushroom is so prominent in the Old Growth forests, effective as an antimicrobial agent and immune enhancer, shows that *G. applanatum* is a steward not only for the ecological health of the woodlands but for its human inhabitants.

Ganoderma lucidum (Wm. Curtis: Fries) Karsten

Common Names
Reishi, Mannentake, Ling Zhi or Ling Chi, Varnished Conk

Distribution and Natural Habitat
This mushroom is widely distributed throughout the world, from the Amazon through the southern regions of North America and across much of Asia, less frequently found in temperate than in the sub-tropical regions. An annual, growing on a wide variety of woods, typically on dead or dying trees, primarily on deciduous woods, especially oak, maple, elm, willow, sweetgum, magnolia, locust, and in the Orient, on plum. Found on stumps, especially near the soil interface, and occasionally on soils arising from buried roots. Occurring from May through November, and more common in warmer temperate regions. In the southeastern and southwestern United States, *Ganoderma lucidum* is frequently found in oak forests. In the northeastern states, this species is most common in maple groves.

Known Active Constituents
ß-Glucans, Hetero-ß-glucans,
ß-(1—6)-glucuronoglucan
Mannogalactoglucan
Ganoderans
Ganoderic & ganoderenic acids—triterpenes
Ling Zhi-8 Protein

Form Used
Fruiting bodies
Spores

Mycelia grown on grain
Mycelia grown in liquid fermentation

Medicinal Properties

Immune enhancing, Reishi primarily acts as a biological response modifier, stimulating macrophage (interleukins 1,2 6, 10) production, activating the host's production of natural killer, T cells and tumor necrosis factors. Although directly active as an antimicrobial (Suay et al., 2000), most studies show Reishi mushrooms are not generally as directly tumoricidal against most cancers compared to many other mushroom species (Ooi et al. 2002).

Anti-tumor, anti-viral, cholesterol reducing, anti-fatiguing (Wasser & Weis, 1999; Mizuno, 1995; Soo, 1994; Yang & Wang, 1994; Kim et al., 1994; Yang et al., 1994; Zhang et al., 1993; Haak-Frendscho, 1993; Furusawa et al. 1992; Jong et al. 1992; Maruyama et al. 1989; Mizuno et al. 1988; Nishitoba et al., 1987; Morigawa et al., 1986; Kodha et al. 1985). More than 100 distinct polysaccharides and 119 triterpenoids have been isolated from this species, both from the mycelia and fruitbodies (Zhou et al. 2002). Many of those that have been studied thus far show immunomodulatory properties, of which only a fraction have been studied.

Triterpenoids—steroid-like compounds that inhibit cholesterol synthesis, allergenic response and histamines—have been detected in extracts of this mushroom (Hirotani et al., 1985). Triterpenoids are more concentrated in the fruitbodies than in the mycelium, a fact of significance for those looking for relief from bronchitis, asthmas and allergies when choosing medicinal mushroom extracts (Han et al., 1998; Zhu et al., 1999, Luo et al., 2002). Lanostanic-type triterpenoids from spores of *G. lucidum* have shown toxicity *in vitro* on the growth of meth-A and LLC tumor cell lines (Min et al., 2000), and cervical HeLa cells (Zhu et al., 2000). Liu et al. (2002) found that germinating or 'broken' spores produced more antitumor agents than dormant spores. Gao et al. (2002) discovered a new cytotoxic lanostanic triterpene aldehyde from the fruitbody of *G. lucidum* showing similar activity to the Min et al. (2000) study. An ethanol fraction isolated from spores, strongly stimulated the activity of T-lymphocytes (Bao et al. (2002).

Studies by Wang et al. (1997) ascertained the primary anti-tumor effects of *Ganoderma lucidum* are from biological response modification of the host. Reishi's polysaccharides caused a 5–29-fold increase in the tumor necrosis factors, interleukin-1 & 6 and a substantial augmentation of T-lymphocytes. *Ganoderma lucidum* has also shown benefits in restoring T-cell function in the spleen of gamma-irradiated mice (Chen et al., 1995). Lieu et al. (1992) reported that polysaccharides of *Ganoderma lucidum* significantly inhibited the growth of leukemia (U937) cells. The anti-oxidizing properties of Reishi have been well established (Chang & But (1987); Chen & Zhang (1987); Wang et al. (1985), Hu et al. (1992), Yang et al. (1992) and Lee et al., 2001. A unique beta glucan from the mycelium enhanced the production of nitric oxides from macrophages but decreased other free radicals and the collateral harm they cause to healthy cells (Han et al., 1998; Li et al., 2000; Zhou & Gao, 2002). This mechanism was further elucidated by Kawakami et al. (2002) who showed that tumor necrosis factors (alpha TNF's) were released by macrophages 8 hours after exposure to derivatives of mushroom polysaccharides, targeting cancerous cells, followed four hours later by a burst of nitric oxide which then killed the diseased cells.

Constituents—including lanostanic triterpenoids—from the fruitbodies of this remarkable species have been shown to be anti-inflammatory (Ukai et al., 1983) in the treatment of arthritis (Stavinoha et al. 1990, 1996; Lin et al., 1993; Mizuno & Kim, 1996; Lee et al. 2001). In one study, Reishi extracts compared favorably with Prednisone® but having few if any negative side effects. In clinical studies with 33 patients, an aqueous extract of this mushroom inhibited platelet-aggregation and gave positive results in treating atherosclerosis (Tao & Feng, 1990). A clinical study (Gau et al. 1990) of 5 HIV-positive hemophiliac patients likewise showed no adverse effects on platelet-aggregation from extracts of *Ganoderma lucidum*, of concern due to the high adenosine fractions found in this mushroom. *Ganoderma lucidum* may prove useful for treating inflammation of the brain (Stavinoha, 1997). Significant results were obtained recently in a clinical study using Reishi components in the treatment of prostate inflammation. (Small et al. 2000). Concurrent with the well-known anti-inflammatory properties of *G. lucidum* is the production of interleukin 2, 6 and interleukin 8 which are typically associated with an inflammatory response of the immune system. This apparent contradiction—an immune enhancer being an anti-inflammatory may be further explained in that the effects of Reishi can be bi-directional at different dosages. Bi-directionality of the ant-inflammatory and immuno-stimulatory effects, as measured by cytokine production, was found to be dose-dependent from the polysaccharides within the closely related *Ganoderma tsugae* in a study by Gao et al. (2000). The possible inflammatory influences may be ameliorated by the production of the steroidal triterpenoids, which are typically anti-inflammatory (Stavinoha et al., 1996). The end result of many studies is that *G. lucidum* is an anti-inflammatory agent and yet an immuno-enhancer. Kim et al. (1999) found that ganoderenic acid A was a potent inhibitor of beta-glucuronidase, an enzyme closely related to liver dysfunction, and may be helpful for those developing cirrhosis from hepatitis. Two small Chinese clinical studies by Zhou & Liu (1990) and Zhu et al. (1992) showed promise in treating chronic hepatitis and post-hepatic cirrhosis, respectively.

Lin et al. (1995) determined that the water extract of fruitbodies of *Ganoderma lucidum* induced free radical scavenging activity. Han et al. (1998), Zhou et al. (2002) and Li et al. (2000) concur that Reishi polysaccharides potentiate the release of nitric oxide while enhancing the scavenging of free radicals by peritoneal macrophages, thus making them less inflammatory while enhancing interleukin, natural killer cell activity, and tumor necrosis factors.

These studies underscore that Reishi may play an important role in anti-aging due to reducing damage from oxidative stress associated with free radicals. Cao et al. (2002) found that polysaccharides from this mushroom regulate the maturation of function of dendritic cells, critical for immune response, while Zhang et al. (2002) isolated yet another bioactive glucose-galactose-mannose sugar enhancing lymphocyte activity and immunoglobulin. Future research may better explain the unique, complex actions of this species and its diverse constituents.

Reishi helps respiration, as this species enhances the oxygen-absorbing capacity of the alveoli in the lungs, thereby enhancing stamina, not unlike ginseng (Chang & But, 1986). Research by Andreacchi et al. (1997) demonstrated that a crude ethanol extract of *Ganoderma lucidum* increased coronary flow due to vasodilatation with a corresponding decrease in diastolic pressure without altering heart rhythm.

Research in Seoul by Dr. Byong Kak Kim (College of Pharmacy, Seoul National University, Korea) showed that extracts of this mushroom prevented the death of lymphocytes infected with HIV and inhibited the replication of the virus within the mother and daughter cells (Kim et al.,1994). In response to hot water extracts of Reishi mushrooms, preserved in ethanol, versus saline controls, NK cell activity was significantly augmented when cancer cells were co-cultured with human spleen cells. (Ohmoto, 2002). A mycelial combination of 7 species grown on rice achieved a similar result, greater than any one species at the same dosage. As the water extract of the fruitbodies is high in beta glucans while the mycelium-on-rice is low in beta glucans, but is high in arabinoxylanes, two causal agents are identified as NK effectors. Both the extract and the heat treated, freeze dried, powdered mycelium from 7 species share common activity levels of enhancing NK activity by 300+%. These compounds may be synergistic. This same combination of 7 species fermented on rice had a strong effect against HIV, inhibiting replication by 99% while the water extract of Reishi fruitbodies was 70%, respectively. These results underscore that water extractions of fruitbodies and oral administration of myceliated rice positively influence the immune system, activating different subsets of immunological receptor sites.

This mushroom has also shown promise in fighting Chronic Fatigue Syndrome (CFS), by enhancing endurance (Aoki et al. 1987; Yang & Wang 1994). Murasugi et al. (1991) isolated and characterized the gene responsible for manufacturing a novel immunomodulating protein ("Ling Zhi 8"). The LD50, an inverse measure of toxicity, is very high with this mushroom, even at relatively large doses (Chen & Miles, 1996), meaning that this mushroom has very low toxicity, making it a strong candidate for immunotherapy.

Comments

Used for more than two millennia, sages and shamans believed the mind and body were fortified by regular consumption of this mushroom in the form of teas that have calming yet fortifying effects. Reishi has been the object of adulation, as is reflected in hundreds of paintings. This fungus came to be called "Mushroom of Immortality." Buddhists had a particular affection for Ling Chi, embellishing their temples with various artistic forms of this highly variable fungus. In Tibet, Himalayan guides have used this mushroom for centuries to help combat high-altitude sickness and infection.

Many strains of Reishi, thought to be *Ganoderma lucidum*, are actually *G. resinaceum*, a nearly identical reddish species which shares in common many of the same antimicrobial properties, inhibiting the growth of *Bacillus subtilis*, *B. pneumoniae*, Staphylococci & Streptococci species. (Sudirman, 1999). They are primarily hardwood saprophytes but some close relatives grow on conifers.

Some research has shown that the application of powdered *Ganoderma* mushrooms may help correct a variety of skin disorders (Naeshiro et al.,1992). In a similar application, a chemist recently claimed that the brown staining mushrooms such as Shiitake and Reishi might be particularly good at curing rashes from poison oak and poison ivy. Asanoma et al., (1994) investigated the use of mushroom as a treatment for some forms of skin cancer. Although *Ganoderma lucidum* is the best known, many other relatives possess medicinal properties, and are currently being studied. Of particular interest are the conifer-degrading species, specifically *Ganoderma applanatum Ganoderma oregonense* and *Ganoderma tsugae* (Zhang et al, 1994; Mizuno et al., 1995a). An interesting article by Hung et al. (2000) explores the use of a weavable skin substitute made from fruitbody of *G. tsugae*, promoting the healing of surface wounds. This remarkable discovery illustrates how fungal-friendly our bodies are to this group. *Ganoderma lucidum* and its allies (*G. formosanum, G. neo-japanicum, G. capense*) have strong free-radical scavenging properties (Lin et al. 1995), and continue to be the subject of studies worldwide.

I cultivate many varieties of *Ganoderma lucidum*. They can be grown indoors or outdoors, generally preferring warm temperatures typical of the sub-tropics. Their beauty and forms are timeless, striking a deep chord in many who are awestruck by the fruitings in my growing rooms. The dualistic incurving forms of the Reishi caps, with its spiraling patterns of symmetrical growth rings, invoke a sense of peace and infinity. For a mushroom to be both beautiful and medicinally powerful is a wonder of nature.

Grifola frondosa   (Dicks: Fr.) S.F.Gray

= *Polyporus frondosus* Dick ex. Fr.

Common Names
Maitake, Kumotake ("Cloud Mushroom"), Mushikusa Hen-of-the-Woods

Distribution and Natural Habitat
Growing in northern temperate, deciduous forests. In North America, primarily found in Eastern Canada and

throughout the Northeastern and Mid-Atlantic States. Rarely found in the northwestern and in the southeastern United States. Also indigenous to the northeastern regions of Japan, the temperate hardwood regions of China and Europe where this species was first used as a food and medicine.

Found on stumps or at the base of dead or dying deciduous hardwoods, especially oak, elm, maple, blackgum, beech, and occasionally on larch.

Known Active Constituents
Beta-glucans
1--6 ß-glucan (Grifolan)
1--4 ß-D-glucans
1--3 ß-D-glucans
Acidic ß-glucans
Hetero ß-glucans
Mannogalactofucan
Mannoxyloglucan
Xyloglucan
N-acetylgalactosamine-specific lectin ("GFL")

Form Used
Fruiting bodies
Mycelia grown on grain
Fermented mycelia

Medicinal Properties

Anti-tumor (especially breast, prostate & colorectal cancer), anti-diabetic, anti-viral (currently the subject of research in the treatment of HIV) (Nanba, 1997; Nanba et al., 1992; Nanba 1993; 1995; Mori et al., Yamada et al. 1990; 1987; Kawagishi et al. 1990, Ohno, 1984, 1986; and Suzuki, 1984).

In a non-randomized clinical study of 165 advanced stage (III–IV) cancer patients, "tumor regression or significant symptom improvements were observed in 11 of 15 breast-cancer patients, 12 out of 18 lung-cancer patients, and 7 of 15 liver-cancer patients. If Maitake were taken in addition to chemotherapy, these response rates improved by 12–28 percent (Nanba,1997, p. 44). A commercial company marketing Maitake extracts announced its approval from the FDA for IND (Investigational New Drug Application) for a Phase II pilot study on the effect of an extract from Maitake on advanced breast and prostate cancer patients (Maitake Products, Inc.,

1998). Maitake beta-glucans increase tumor necrosis factors in human prostate cancer and are being explored as a treatment (Fullerton et al., 2000). Kodama et al. (2002), in a nonrandomized study, found that patients ranging from 22-57 years in age who had liver, breast and lung cancer showed significant improvement (58%, 68% & 62%, respectively) of immune-competent cells when combined with chemotherapy.

In vitro studies have shown that the 1,3 beta D-glucans, the water-soluble fraction from the fruitbodies, stimulate cytokine production from macrophages, triggering an immune response (Kurashige et al., 1997; Adachi et al. 1998, Okazaki et al., 1995; Adachi, 1994). This group of polysaccharides also stimulates tumor-necrosis factors (Ohno et al., 1995). Investigations into the production of nitric oxides from macrophages exposed to an extract of Maitake mushrooms showed anti-tumor activity (Sanzen et al., 2001). These results concur with those done with Reishi, Cordyceps and other mushrooms.

Maitake has also been implicated as a possible treatment for diabetes (Kubo et al., 1994) by lowering and moderating glucose levels. A study by Manohar et al. (2002) on insulin-resistant mice showed that when a single dose from a Maitake mushroom extract was introduced, circulating glucose lowered by 25%. Konno et al. (2001) and Manohar (2002) suggest that maitake could be an aid in modulating glucose levels in diabetic patients. Dr. Harry Preuss has announced investigations into the use of *Grifola frondosa* for treatment of type II, non-insulin-dependent adult diabetes at Georgetown University.

Comments

This mushroom is a delicious, soft-fleshed polypore with excellent nutritional properties. Of the polypores currently being studied, *Grifola frondosa* is attracting considerable attention from the pharmaceutical industry, especially in Japan and Korea. Several causal compounds appear to be at play, most notably the Beta-glucans, especially the D-fraction constituents. All Maitake mushrooms have within them the D-fractions of Beta-glucans. Ohno et al. (1985) and Takeyama (1987) isolated grifolan from mycelium grown in culture. As the density of the mycelium increases to the eventual creation of a mushroom, so too it is presumed, do the available Beta-glucans.

The Beta-glucans that are contained within the cell walls of Maitake can constitute 10–50% of its dry weight. Structural in nature, these cell wall polysaccharides can decompose into several sub-components, one of which is the well known

(1—6) branched (1—3)-beta-D-glucan having a molecular weight of nearly 1,000,000. The denaturing of the water-soluble, high-molecular-weight polysaccharides to lighter subcomponents through digestion and/or moderate heat treatment (>100° C = > 212° F) can enhance the bioavailability of grifolan and its synergistic cousins. However, excess heat—over 250° C (= 302° F)—can reduce (1—6) branched (1—3) Beta-glucans into smaller sub fractions (ranging from 6400 to 250,000 m.w.) which, when isolated from one another, showed reduced or little activity (Mizuno & Zhuang, 1995; Adachi et al., 1990). Hence, heat treatment between 100-121° C. (212-250° F.) is well within the target range for making these compounds extractable and/or bio-available without degradation into inactive constituents.

The transformation Maitake undergoes from gray mounds, brain-like balls into labyrinthine folds, petals, and maturing into extended leaflets is one of nature's great displays of grace and being. We grow Maitake indoors on alder sawdust (*Alnus rubra, Betulaceae family*), supplemented with organic oat bran, and have developed several novel fruiting strains from mushrooms collected in the wild. Maitake is one of my favorite mushrooms. My body hungers for the taste of this mushroom, which I think is a reflection of its inherent beneficial properties. I like combining Maitake, Reishi, Shiitake, and others to make an immune-enhancing mushroom tea. For more information on the cultivation of this mushroom, see my book *Growing Gourmet & Medicinal Mushrooms*, Ten Speed Press, Berkeley.

Inonotus obliquus   (Pers.: Fr.) Pilat

= *Polyporus obliquus* Pers.:Fr.

= *Poria oblique* (Pers.:Fr.) Pilat

Common Names
Clinker Polypore, Clinker Fungus, Cinder Conk, Chaga, Charga, Tschaga, Tschagapilz, Kabanoanatake, Black Mass

Distribution and Natural Habitat
Circumpolar, widespread throughout boreal forests, primarily on birch, but also found on beech, elm, ash and rarely on

ironwood. Growing on living and dead trees and stumps, causing a white heart rot.

Known Active Constituents
Protein-bound polysaccharides
  Xylogalactoglucan
Lanostanoid triterpenoids & other steroidals
  (betulin flanosterols, Inotodiol
Inositols (vitamin B)
Lactones
Melanin

Form Used
Fruiting bodies, boiled in water
Freeze dried mycelia grown on grain
Extracted fermented mycelia

Medicinal Properties
Anti-tumor, water-soluble and water insoluble hetero-polysaccharides, protein-bound polysaccharides and lanostanic triterpenoids, including inosotidiol, betulin and ergosterol peroxides. More proteins are in the mycelia than are in the fruitbodies. Hypoglycemic effects were measured from the ethanol soluble fraction (Mizuno et al. 1999). Approved as an anti-cancer drug ('befungin') in Russia as early as 1955 and reportedly successful in treating breast, lung, cervical, and stomach cancers (Hobbs, 1995). A study Ryzmowka (1998) found that the water extract of *I. obliquus* inhibited the growth of cervical cancer cells *in vitro*. Burczk et al. (1996) noted that some of this mushroom's constituents had a limiting effect on cell divisions of cancerous cells. Mizuno et al. (1996) and Kahlos et al. (1996) noted that crude fractions from this mushroom showed anti-viral activity against HIV and influenza respectively. Shin et al. (2000a, 2000b, & 2000c) and Kahlos et al. (1984, 1987a, 1987b, 1988 & 1990) have extensively analyzed this species for its chemical constituents, finding suites of lanostanic triterpenoids and triterpenes, many of which are bioactive.

Comments
A distinctive fungus causing a black cankerous mass (sclerotium) on birch trees, this mushroom attracted the attention of Eurasians centuries ago (Maret, 1991). Used traditionally

for treatment of tuberculosis ("consumption"), ulcers, digestive, heart and liver cancers, the brittle Chaga was de-skinned of its black outer mass, boiled and used as a tea. About 3-5 grams of dried mushroom per pot of tea was used. Once a tea was made, the boiled mass can be pounded into a poultice to prevent infection and help recovery from cellular damage. Historically, this mushroom also enjoyed the reputation as an analgesic with anti-inflammatory properties. Recent research from Japan (Ohtomo, 2002) shows this mushroom, like many of polypores, has strong immunomodulatory activities, regulating cytokine and interleukin response pathways.

Chaga concentrates betulin from the bark of birch trees, just as *Taxomyces andreanae* concentrates taxol from the bark of the Pacific Yew tree. Kahlos et al (1996) found the external black skin of the *Chaga sclerotia* had 30% betulin while the internal portions contained fungal lanostanes. This study suggests that teas would be better made from whole Chaga that was not de-skinned. Betulin, sourced from birch bark and/or Chaga, also has shown promise in treating malignant melanoma, completely inhibiting tumors implanted in mice, and causing apoptosis of cancerous cells (Pisha et al., 1995; Duke, 1999). That a natural medicine in the form of a *Chaga sclerotium* could be so compact allows for the portability of this medicine in ancient times, making it a valuable asset in the pharmacopoeia of pre-modern peoples.

Phellinus linteus (Berk. et Curt.) Aoshima

= *Phellinus linteus* (Berk. et Curt.) Teng

Common Names
Meshimakobu (Japanese), Meshima/ Mesima, Sangwhang (Chinese), Black Hoof

Distribution and Natural Habitat
Circumpolar in its distribution, primarily a sub-tropical and tropical species on oaks, poplars, mulberries, and some pines, causing a white rot. So named for its presence on Meshima Island (the Island of the Woman) of Nagasaki Perfecture—and grows on broadleaf trees. Widely distributed in the southern United States, this mushroom is rare in the more temperate

regions of North America, according to Gilbertson & Ryvarden (1986).

Known Active Constituents
Polysaccharides
Heteroglycopeptides
Cyclophellitol
Ergosterol (provitamin D2) derivatives

Form Used
Fruiting bodies, boiled in water
Mycelia grown on grain
Mycelia from fermentation

Medicinal Properties
Anti-tumor (Han et al., 1995) and immuno-modulating (Kim et al., 1996). An early study by Sasaki et al. (1971) explored its tumor-retarding properties. Water-soluble fractions from the fruitbodies and the mycelium of *Phellinus linteus* have immune stimulating activity (Lee et al.,1996) specifically enhancing B-lymphocytes (Song et al.,1995). Novel types of beta-glucan polysaccharides have been identified which enhanced a host-mediated immune response (Han et al., 1998). Ikekawa (1968, 2001) noted that water fractions of this mushroom did not inhibit the growth of implanted, solid-type sarcoma tumors in mice. Conversely, Mizuno et al. (2000) found that this mushroom had the highest rate of inhibition against implanted sarcoma 180 tumors in mice, resulting in 96.7% inhibition. Furthermore, Mizuno reported clinical studies at Seoul University which found, post chemotherapy with 45 stomach cancer patients, significantly enhanced NK activity and resulting in recovery of T-3 and T-4 lymphocytes to near-normal conditions. Research by Song et al. (1995) and Kim et al. (1996) reported that the water extract from the mycelium induced B-lymphocytes, and enhanced cellular immunity. Kim's study noted that the activity of the polysaccharides from the mycelium had a wider range of activity and greater antitumor effects than polysaccharides isolated from other mushroom species. Han et al. (1999) found that polysaccharides from Meshima, when combined with the chemotherapeutic agent adriamycin, increased effectiveness against tumor growth and metastasis, while the polysaccharides by themselves did not influence the growth of pulmonary cancers in mice. A novel beta-glucosidase inhibitor, called cyclophellitol, has been isolated from this fungus (Atsumi et al.,1990; Withers et al.,1991). Shon & Nam

(2001) explored the anti-mutagenic properties from the mycelium and fruitbodies, showing activity in limiting or preventing Carcinogenesis.

Comments

Meshima is a hard polypore with a hoof-like cap—nearly black in color on top while yellowish brown underneath, producing a brilliant golden mycelium in culture. Used in Korea to prevent the recurrence of cancer, the mycelium and the fruitbodies provide active constituents. Well studied by Korean researchers in the past few years, and becoming increasingly popular as a treatment for cancer, this mushroom is becoming a popular adjuvant with chemotherapies. Numerous studies, many of them in Korean journals, have been published on its unique medicinal properties. *Phellinus linteus* is similar to several woody conks in the genus Phellinus and Fomes that have been used by native peoples for medicinal purposes, (Saar, 1991). The research on Meshima is a good example of how bioactive the components of the mycelium and its suitability for immunotherapy are compared to the difficult-to-collect fruitbodies.

Piptoporus betulinus (Bull.:Fr.) Karst.

= *Polyporus betulinus* (Bull.:Fr.) Fr.

Common Names
Kanbatake, Birch Polypore

Distribution and Natural Habitat
Found throughout the birch forests of the world, circumboreal, and one of the most common mushrooms on that host.

Known Active Constituents
Betulin,
Betulinic acid
Agaric acid

Single stranded RNA
Heteroglucans
Antibiotics

Form Used
Mushrooms
Mycelium on grain
Fermented mycelium

Medicinal Properties
Crude extracts and purified fraction are tumor inhibiting *in vitro*. The novel antibiotic, Piptamine, has been isolated from this fungus (Schlegel et al. 2000). Pisha et al. (1995) found, in mice studies, that betulinic acid, a pentacyclic triterpene, was specifically toxic to melanoma without adverse effects to the host. Farnsworth et al. (1995) found that betulinic acid facilitated apoptosis of melanoma. This compound has been further evaluated for the treatment or prevention of malignant melanoma. Manez et al. (1997) found that selected triterpenoids reduced chronic dermal inflammation.

Comments
Found with the famous Ice Man, the use of *P. betulinus* transcends cultures and millennia. A fungus useful to stop bleeding, prevent bacterial infection, and as an antimicrobial agent against intestinal parasites, this species is one of the most prominent and frequently encountered mushrooms seen on birch. Capasso (1998) postulated that the Ice Man used this fungus to treat infection from intestinal parasites (*Trichuris trichiura*)

Akihisa T. et al. (2002) determined that a common woodland fungus, *Chaetomium longirostre*, could transform betulin into derivatives showing tumor retarding properties. The hypothesis is that biotransformation by other microorganisms may activate other properties locked within this species.

Polyporus umbellatus Fr.

= *Grifola umbellata*
(Pers.: Fr.) Donk
= *Dendropolyporus umbellatus*
(Pers.:Fr.) Julich

Common Names
Umbrella Polypore, Zhu Ling, Chu Ling, Chorei, Choreimaitake

Distribution and Natural Habitat
Infrequently occurring throughout the deciduous woodlands of north central and northeastern North America, in the temperate regions of China, and in Europe where it was first described. Found on the ground, arising from dead roots or buried wood, on stumps, or in soils rich in lignicolous matter, preferring birches, maples, willows and beeches.

Known Active Constituents
ß-Glucans

Form Used
Sclerotia
Mycelium grown on grain
Fermented mycelium

Medicinal Properties
Anti-tumor (lung, bladder, liver) immune enhancement, anti-malarial, anti-inflammatory, liver protectant (hepatitis B), and diuretic (Yang et al.,1994; Huang,1993; Zhu, 1987; Chang & But 1986; Haranaka et al. 1985; Ito and Shimura, 1985; Lin et al. 1988; Miyaski 1983; Chang 1978, 1983; Lovy et al. 1999).

Studies in China have shown that this mushroom is particularly effective in helping the immune system rebound after chemotherapy and radiation therapy in the treatment of lung cancer (Chang & But, 1986). Chinese clinical studies with 146 patients (Yang et al. 1994) have shown that the recurrence of bladder cancer was reduced by nearly 50% with the use of *Polyporus umbellatus* over an average period of 70 months, while 68% showed no recurrence in an earlier study spanning an average of 26 months (Yang 1991). Cytotoxic properties against Sarcoma-180-induced liver tumor cells have also been reported (You et al., 1994). In a clinical study of 90 patients, Xiong (1993) and Yan (1988) found that *Polyporus umbellatus* was effective in the treatment of chronic hepatitis B. Several compounds limiting the growth of leukemia 1210 cells *in vitro* have been isolated from the fruitbodies of this mushroom (Ohsawa, 1992). Zhong et al. (1991) isolated polysaccharides, which enhanced the cellular immunity of mice with liver lesions. You et al. (1994) found that oral administration of Zhu Ling extracts functionally double the lifespan of liver-tumor bearing mice.

Comments

Strongly anti-tumor and containing potent natural antibiotics, this species has figured prominently in Traditional Chinese Medicine (TCM). Most commonly known as a diuretic and useful for the treatment of urinary-tract infections (Li et al.,1992), *Polyporus umbellatus* contains powerful immunomodulating compounds and has also been implicated in the limiting of leukemia (1210) cell proliferation (Ohsawa et al. 1992). Lovy et al. (1999) found that extracts of this mushroom inhibited the growth of T-4 leukemia cells and was 100% effective against *Plasmodium falciparum*, the malarial parasite *in vitro*. Since this species forms sclerotia underground, and mushrooms are known to concentrate heavy metals, collection or cultivation of this mushroom in environments with a background contamination of heavy metals is a concern. Sclerotia of this mushroom, usually thinly sliced, are widely sold in Chinese apothecaries. That a resting, fungal mass can remain in wet ground contact for a year or more, and not rot, underscores its antimicrobial properties.

Schizophyllum commune Fr.

Common Names
Suehirotake, Split Gill Polypore

Distribution and Natural Habitat
Widely distributed throughout the world on deciduous branches and fallen trees, and on lumber made from the same, growing throughout the year above freezing temperatures. This is one of the most common mushrooms in the world.

Known Active Constituents
Beta glucans
Sizofilan/Sizofiran
Schizophyllan
Sonifilan
Arabinoxylanes by consequence of enzymatic conversion.

Form Used
Primarily mycelium that has been grown on rice, or mycelium extracted via fermentation. This author is unaware of any studies using the fruitbodies as the base material from which medicinal constituents have been isolated.

Medicinal Properties
The molecular constituents within the mycelial cell walls have been the subject of several extensive clinical trials in combination with chemo- and radiation therapies in treating cervical, lung and gastric cancers. One of the first human studies, published in the *European Journal of Cancer* was by Fujimoto et al. (1984), who showed that, when treating 326 patients with gastric cancer, only those at Stage III showed statistically significant improvement. Sakagami et al. (1988) found that the anti-tumor polysaccharide schizophyllan increased interleukin 2 and induced gamma interferons. Baseline studies using mice showed promise in the treatment of squamous-cell carcinomas (Arika et al., 1986) and cervical and lung cancers (Inomata et al., 1990). Usui et al. (1995) examined the cytotoxic factors from marine macrophages in response to schizophyllan and its

derivatives. Hasegawa et al. (1990) reported that use of sizofiran enhanced immune response in those patients with uterine cancer, and being treated with chemotherapy, increasing the cytotoxic activities of macrophages and natural killer cells. In a similar, later study with 386 patients, Fujimoto et al., (1991) found that patients who underwent curative surgery, in combination with anti-tumor drugs and sizofiran, had a better prognosis for survival than the controls. A randomized study of 312 patients with advanced cervical carcinoma (stage IV) showed that sizofiran is an effective immunotherapeutic agent, helping the immune system recover from the effects of radiation therapy (Miyazaki et al., 1995). In a small clinical study of 15 cancer patents, tracked over 5 years, results showed that use of sizofilan as an adjuvant in the treatment of neck cancer with radiation therapy increased survival rates to 86.7% from 73.4% in the control group (Kimura et al., 1994).

Comments

This mushroom is a bridge species between gilled mushrooms and polypores—hence, its name, the Split-gill Polypore. A prominent woodland species, *S. commune* has been the subject of intense mycological inquiries, beginning with its genetic and sexual mating characteristics. The spores of this fungus have caused lung and brain infections or mycoses, although rarely, with those who have compromised immune systems being more susceptible (Lacaz et al., 1996; Rhis et al., 1996). However, the processed forms of this fungus through heat-sterilization converts this fungus, transforming it from a human pathogen into a human medicine. Sterilization neutralizes the cells and tenderizes the exoskeleton of the mycelium into a more bio-available form. Most, if not all, medicinal products from this species are mycelially based, and are not grown to the point of sporulation. Nevertheless, this author believes that, products from this species must be presented in a biologically neutralized form, such as achieved through heat sterilization, so that any potential pathogenicity is prevented and medicinal properties can be unleashed. Products not sterilized or presented in a cell-free form, could be potentially infectious through exposure to hyphal fragmentation. Free flying cells of mycelium—called hyphae—can be viable, and re-grow.

Trametes versicolor   (L:Fr.) Pilat

= *Coriolus versicolor* (L.: Fr.) Quelet
= *Polyporus versicolor* L.:Fr.

Common Names
Turkey Tail, Yun Zhi, Kawaratake

Distribution and Natural Habitat
Found throughout North America and apparently, circumpolar, widely distributed throughout the boreal, temperate, subtropical and tropical regions of the world. Few mushrooms can boast such adaptivity, and variety of forms—hence the name 'versicolor.' Turkey Tail is the most common polypore on dead hardwoods, more rarely on conifers. Most shiitake cultivators have encountered this fungus, as it is a common competitor on natural logs.

Known Active Constituents
ß-glucans
PSK (protein bound polysaccharide, ß-(1-4)-D-glucan protein)
PSP (polysaccharopeptide)
Ergosterol (provitamin D2) derivatives

Form Used
Fruiting bodies
Mycelium grown on grain
Mycelium in fermentation

Medicinal Properties
Immune enhancement, anti-tumor, anti-viral, anti-bacterial, anti-oxidant (Ebin & Murata, 1994; Tochikura et al., 1987; Yang & Kwok, 1993; Ng et al. 1996).

Trametes versicolor is the source of PSK, commercially known as "Krestin," responsible for several hundred million dollars of sales as an approved anticancer drug in Asia. In clinical studies of 224 patients (Sugimachi et al., 1997), and 262 patients (Nakazato et al., 1994) afflicted with gastric cancer and treated with chemotherapy followed by a regimen using the protein bound polysaccharide ('PSK') from *Trametes versicolor*, the results showed a decrease in recurrence, an increase in the disease-free survival rate of the patients, and was clearly cost-effective. PSK stimulated interleukin-1 production by human cells (Sakagami et al. 1993). Extracts of this mushroom, particularly PSK, have been found to impart a chemo protective defense to healthy cells while sensitizing cancerous cells (Kobayashi et al., 1993; Kim et al., 1999).

A highly water soluble, low molecular weight cytotoxic polysaccharopeptide ("PSP") isolated from this mushroom has anti-viral agent inhibiting HIV replication based on an *in vitro* study (Collins and Ng, 1997). PSP is a classic biological response modifier (BRM), inducing gamma interferon, interleukin-2 and T-cell proliferation, differing chemically from PSK in that it has rhamnose and arbinose while PSK has fucose. (Ng 1998) Dong et al. (1996, 1997) reported that a polysaccharide peptide ("CVP") and its refined form ("RPSP") has not only anti-tumor properties, but elicits an immunomodulating response by inhibiting the proliferation of human leukemia (HL-60) cells while not affecting the growth of normal human peripheral lymphocytes. Yang et al. (1992) also found that a smaller polypeptide ("SPCV," 10,000 m.w.) significantly inhibited the growth of leukemia cells. Kariya et al. (1992) and Kobayashi et al. (1994) showed that the protein-bound polysaccharides of *Trametes versicolor* result in the expression of superoxide dismutases, and consequently have antioxidizing activities against free radicals.

Comments

Probably the best-documented medicinal mushroom, wild strains of *Trametes versicolor* (=*Coriolus versicolor*) typically show remarkable vitality and aggressiveness in culture. The commercial drug, PSK, is derived primarily from mycelial cultures, but can be extracted from the actual fruitbodies (mushrooms). The activity is two-fold: both as an anti-tumor compound, inhibiting growth of cancer cells, and in stimulating a host mediated response, bolstering the immune system's natural killer cells (Garcia-Lora et al., 2001). Lin et al. (1996) showed that *Coriolus versicolor* polysaccharides ("CVP") enhanced the recovery of spleen cells subsequent to gamma irradiation. Used clinically in the treatment of cervical cancer in conjunction with radiation therapy, PSK has helped substantially to increase survival rates. Recent studies at the New York Medical College suggest that ethanolic extracts of Yun Zhi show promise as an adjuvant therapy in treating hormone responsive prostate cancer by slowing tumorigenesis (Hsieh et al., 2001). This species, or its derivatives, have been also been used to treat a wide variety of cancers (breast, lung, colon, sarcoma, carcinoma).

Trametes versicolor's PSK has potent anti-microbial activities against *Escherichia coli, Listeria monocytogenes,* and *Candida albicans.* (Tsukagoshi et al. 1984; Sakagami et al. 1991). The mycelium and the fruitbody—comprised of compacted, differentiated mycelium—also produces anti-microbial compounds, natural defenses preventing rot. Hence, its traditional use in teas and soups seems well warranted as an antimicrobial additive to human diet, especially in pre-modern times. A report by Ikekawa (2001) showed that an extract (PSK) was ineffective as an anti-tumor agent with implanted Sarcoma 180 tumors while aqueous extracts from fleshier mushrooms like Shiitake (*Lentinula edodes*), Enoki (*Flammulina velutipes*) and Oyster (*Pleurotus ostreatus*) elicited a strong host mediated response, leading to significant regression of tumors. Ikekawa further states, "although extracts of *Trametes versicolor* was approved as an anti-cancer drug in Japan and that of *P. linteus* in Korea, they are not very active in oral administration (p.o.) experiments" (Ikekawa, 2001, pg. 293). In contrast to Reishi, aqueous extracts of *T. versicolor* and PSK appear to be ineffective in controlling Sarcoma 180, but may be effective against other forms of cancer, and/or when whole fractions, not isolated fractions, are employed. PSK has been used to normalize immune function in patients with chronic rheumatoid arthritis (Hobbs, 1995).

Several small U.S. clinical studies by Ghoneum (1995,1995,1998) using a constellation of the mycelia of three mushroom species, one of which was *T. versicolor*, showed increases in NK cells and decreases in tumor associated antigens of prostatic and breast cancer patients from oral ingestion. These studies used powdered mycelium grown on a rice carrier, a method by which the extracellular enzymes secreted by the fungal cells create arabinoxylanes by converting glucose and rice bran. Beta-glucans and other polysaccharides are present but in lower levels than that found in the fruitbodies. However, ergosterols—provitamin D—are much higher. The complex constituents within the mycelial-grain product may be synergistic, resulting in a cascade of immune related defenses. This combination is orally active; eliciting a host mediated immune response. PSK-isolated studies rely upon one isolated fraction.

Teethed Fungi

The teethed fungi have many representatives, some of which are exquisitely delicious. Species belonging to the genus *Hericium* are most notable. *Hericium erinaceus* and *Hericium coralloides* produce prodigiously in culture and are the most flavorful. *Hericium abietis*, a lover of conifers, is more difficult to cultivate. This group of mushrooms, with their snow-white, distinctive appearance has long been a favorite of woodspeople. Like Shiitake, the cultivation of this mushroom probably evolved from the assiduous efforts of those who first collected them wild. We know now they have not only unique anti-tumor and antibiotical properties, but some of these same compounds can play essential roles in repairing cell damage, especially in stimulating nerve regeneration.

Hericium erinaceus (Bulliard: Fries) Persoon

= *Hericium erinaceum* (Fr.) Pers.

Common Names

Monkey's Head, Lion's Mane, Yamabushitake, Houtou

Distribution and Natural Habitat

Reported from North America, Europe, China and Japan. On dying or dead oak, walnut, beech, maple, sycamore and other broad-leaf trees. Found most frequently on logs or stumps. Distinctive and easy to identify.

Known Active Constituents

Cyathane derivatives
Erinacines, Hericenones
Beta-D-glucans
Galactoxyloglucan
Glucoxylan
Mannoglucoxylan
Xylan
Ergosterol—provitamin D2

45

Form Used

Fruiting bodies
Mycelium grown on grain
Fermented mycelia

Medicinal Properties

Anti-cancer, immune stimulation, nerve growth regeneration, anti-microbial, Parkinson's disease and used for the treatment of atrophic gastritis (Mizuno et al 1992, 1995; Okamoto et al.,1993; Xu, HM., 1994, Kawagishi et al. 1991 & 1994; Matsui et al. 1990, Xu, 1985).

Comments

In Traditional Chinese Medicine, this species has been prescribed for stomach ailments and for prevention of cancer in the GI tract. Dr. Mizuno, Shizuoka University, isolated a group of acid derivatives, which are strongly effective against hepatoma cells. He further identified five distinct polysaccharides with potent anti-tumor properties that extended the life spans of the patients (Mizuno, 1995). Recently another group of Japanese researchers patented an extraction process, which isolates Nerve Growth Stimulant (NGS) factor—compounds now known as erinacines (Kawagishi et al., 1991, 1994). A novel erinacine, Erinacine Q, isolated from liquid culture, is one precursor to this family of erinacines (Kenmoku et al. 2002). These compounds stimulate neurons to re-grow, a feat of great significance in the possible treatment for senility and Alzheimer's disease, repairing neurological trauma, increasing cognitive abilities and perhaps improving muscle/motor response pathways.

Once reserved for the palates of the royal families, this delectable mushroom not only has unique medicinal properties, but also is popular for its distinctive seafood-like flavor. Primarily a hardwood saprophyte, *Hericium erinaceus* is widely distributed throughout the world. For techniques on the cultivation of this and other medicinal mushrooms, please consult *Growing Gourmet & Medicinal Mushrooms*.

Gilled Mushrooms

The gilled species comprise the largest taxonomic group in mushrooms. Classic examples are Button, Shiitake, Oyster, and Enoki mushrooms. The gilled mushrooms can be found in every habitat, from fields to forest, from the tropics to the Arctic. Mycologists now believe that many gilled mushrooms evolved from polypores. The fact that they share some of the same complexes of medicinal compounds underscores this close kinship.

Agaricus blazei Murrill

Common Names
Royal Sun Agaricus, Himematsutake, Kawariharatake, Songrong

Distribution and Natural Habitat

Growing in the southeastern United States, first reported from Florida, *Agaricus blazei* is a relatively rare mushroom and infrequently encountered. In Brazil, in the Sal Hose do Rio Preto district, northwest of Sao Paulo city, this mushroom is common in the fields and mountainous regions. A constellation of strains—probably more widely distributed than the literature presently indicates—cluster around this iconoclastic species. Growing in soils rich in woody debris, in mixed woods, well-composted soils, and along forest-field interfaces.

Known Active Constituents
Ergosterol (provitamin D2) derivatives
Double-stranded RNA
α-(1—4)-, ß-(1—6)-glucan
α-(1—6)-, α-(1—4)-glucan
ß-(1—3)-D-glucan, ß-(1—4)-α-D-glucan, ß-(1—6)-D-glucan
ß-(1—2)-, ß-(1—3)-glucomannan
Glucomannan/Mannogalactoglucan
Proteoglucans
Riboglucans

Form Used

Fruiting bodies
Mycelium grown on grain
Mycelium in fermentation

Medicinal Properties

Anti-tumor (particularly uterocervical), immune enhancing, interferon and interleukin enhancing, anti-viral, cholesterol reducing, and blood sugar modulating (Mizuno, 1995; Mizuno et al., 1989; Kawagishi et al., 1988.). Induction of alpha tumor necrosis factors, interleukin and nitric oxide expression from macrophages was found by Sorimachi et al. (2001) in the ethanol precipitate from an extract of the mycelium. Kawakami et al. (2002) found that macrophages secreted alpha tumor necrosis factors 8 hours after exposure to *A. blazei* polysaccharide fractions, and 4 hours thereafter, produced nitric oxide target specific to the now weakened cancer cells. Takaku et al. (2001) also identified another alcohol-soluble, lipid fraction from this mushroom with high oral activity—which his team subsequently identified as being heavy in ergosterol, provitamin D-1. Osaki et al. (1994) reported on the anti-mutagenic and bactericidal properties, particularly against Salmonella. Both the water-soluble and water-insoluble fractions show promise in the treatment of cancer (Mizuno et al. 1998). A novel protein-bound polysaccharide ("ATOM") showed no cytotoxic activity against four cancers *in vitro* but had pronounced activity against these same cancers *in vivo*, suggesting a host-mediated response (Ito et al, 1997). A novel tumoricidal agent comprised of 90% + glucose, with a molecular mass of 380,000, has been isolated from this species and *in vivo* retards tumor growth (Fujimiya et al., 1998). Kawagishi et al. (1988) isolated a water-insoluble polysaccharide with anti-tumor activity having a molecular weight of approximately 10,000. Ito et al. (1994, 1997) isolated a novel polysaccharide-protein complex, which proved to be highly active against a variety of implanted cancers in mice. The isolated constituent had no cytotoxic effect against the growth of tumors *in vitro* but was highly effec-tive against mouse-implanted tumors at doses ranging from 10-100 mg/kg/day, suggesting a host-mediated response.

Comments

First collected by the American mycologist Murrill (1945) from the southeastern United States and re-collected by Heinemann (1993) in Brazil, this warm-weather mushroom species is the center of a constellation of strains, and is closely related to *Agaricus subrufescens*. The cultivation of this mushroom was pioneered by Japanese mycologists from specimens collected from Brazil, taken back to Japan. Riding a wave of popularity for its reputedly strong anti-tumor properties, *Agaricus blazei* has an almond flavor and often stains golden when handled or cut. Once reported by Mizuno (1985) to have more beta-glucans than any other mushroom then analyzed at the National Cancer Center Laboratory in Tokyo (Mizuno, 1985), we now know many other medicinal mushrooms have higher percentages of these active constituents.

Although human studies have not been completed, this species is a new star in the potential treatment of cancer. This mushroom also contains compounds that inhibit the enzyme aromatase. Aromatase is associated with tumor growth. Compounds inhibiting aromatase have potential for the treatment or prevention of breast cancer (Bankhead, 1999). One contradiction remains unresolved: *Agaricus blazei* also contains carcinogens— agaritines—approximately 1% of dried mass in the fruitbodies. Products from the mycelium vary substantially— from < .02% to .2%, depending upon the manufacturer and source (Stijve, 2001). Agaritines are hydrazines, that, when metabolized, are converted into highly carcinogenic sub-derivatives. Studies have not yet delimited the mitigating effects of agaritine on this mushroom's medicinal properties. Specialized processing treatments can remove agaritines while not adversely affecting the beneficial properties of this mushroom. Consumers should beware that many of the *A. blazei* products being sold contain these potentially dangerous hydrazines. Techniques for the cultivation of this culinary/medicinal mushroom are described by Stamets (2000). Stijve et al. (2001) note that two varieties of this species are sufficiently different to warrant the creation of a new species. Close examination of the forms growing in the United States and Japan are being compared to those found in Brazil (Wasser, 2002).

Flammulina velutipes (Curtis ex Fries) Singer

= *Collybia velutipes* (Fr.) Quelet

Common Names
Enokitake, Enokidake, Golden Needle Mushroom, Jin Zhen Gu

Distribution and Natural Habitat
Widespread throughout the temperate regions of the world, growing from sea level to tree line. Primarily on hardwoods, occasionally on conifers, commonly growing in the late fall through early winter.

Known Active Constituents
ß-Glucan-proteins
ß-Glycoprotein "Proflamin"

Form Used
Fruiting bodies
Mycelia grown on grain
Fermented mycelium

Medicinal Properties
Low-molecular-weight polysaccharides have been shown to strongly stimulate host-mediated anti-tumor responses via oral administration (Nakahara et al., 1967). An alkaline-soluble polysaccharide (approx. 200,000 m.w.) triggered splenic lymphocyte production in mice and exhibited potent anti-tumor activity *in vivo* but not *in vitro* (Leung et al.,1997), while a new immunomodulating protein that stimulates the production of human peripheral blood lymphocytes has been isolated (Ko et al., 1995). Enokitake has been implicated as a possible treatment for lymphoma, Sarcoma 180, B-16 melanoma, and prostate cancer. Enoki mushrooms also contain blood pressure lowering (Kabir & Kimura, 1987) and cholesterol reducing compounds (Fukushima et al. 2001).

Suay et al. (2000) found that extracts from the fruitbodies of this mushroom inhibited the growth of the bacterium, *Bacillus subtilis*, but was not effective against other bacteria

Enterrococcus faecium, Pseudomonas aeruginosa, Mycobacterium smegmatis, and the fungi *Aspergillus fumigatus, Candida albicans*, and *Saccharomyces cervesiae*. That this species produces a target specific antibiotic may be medically significant in the development of future antibiotics.

Comments

Protein-bound polysaccharides isolated from the fruitbodies (mushrooms) are further de-fractionated following oral administration, increasing their effectiveness. This mushroom contains a novel glyco-protein (16,000 m.w.), named "proflamin," isolated from the mycelial cultures. Dr. Ikekawa of the National Cancer Institute of Tokyo conducted an epidemiological survey of Enoki growers and found that their families had a substantially lower cancer rate than the average cancer rate in Japan or that of their surrounding community in Nagano Prefecture (Ikekawa et al., 1989).

Flammulina velutipes is at the center of a constellation of species, including the closely related, aspen-loving *Flammulina populicula*. Considering the close taxonomic relationship these species share, it would not be surprising if many of their medicinal compounds are shared in common.

Lentinula edodes (Berkeley) Pegler

= *Lentinus edodes* (Berkeley) Singer

Common Names
Shiitake, Xiang Gu, Black Forest Mushroom

Distribution and Natural Habitat
Limited to the Far East, native to Japan, Korea, & China. Until recently, not known from North America. This mushroom grows naturally on dead or dying broad-leaf trees, particularly the Shii tree (*Castanopsis cuspidata*), *Pasania spp., Quercus spp.* & and other Asian oaks and beeches.

Known Active Constituents
ß-D-Glucan "lentinan"
Galactoglucomannan
Heteroglucan-protein "LEM"
Eritadenine
Alpha-Mannan Peptide "KS-2"
Glycoproteins
RNA fractions
Ergosterol (provitamin D2)

Form Used
Fruiting bodies
Mycelium grown on grain
Mycelium grown in fermentation

Medicinal Properties
Immuno-modulating (increases natural killer (NK) cell action and interferon), anti-viral, and liver fortifying. Shiitake produces a high-molecular-weight cell-wall sugar called lentinan, which has been used extensively as an injectable anti-cancer drug in Asia. This mushroom has also been studied extensively for its cholesterol reducing, immunostimulating, antibacterial and anti-viral properties (Hirasawa, 1999; Kurashige et al., 1997; Morinaga et al. 1994; Hibino et al., 1994; Oka et al., 1992; Taguchi et al., 1982; Sugano et al., 1982; Chihara, 1969, 1987; Ikekawa et al., 1969). Eritadenine has been shown in laboratory rat studies to significantly reduce cholesterol levels (Sugiyama et al. 1995).

Comments
The most popular and best-studied medicinal mushroom, Shiitake has remained at the center of research since the late 1960's. Lentinan is a high-molecular-weight polysaccharide (ca 500,000 m.w.), free of nitrogen. According to Mizuno et al. (1995a), lentinan has no direct cytotoxic properties but is instrumental in activating a host-mediated response. Macroph-ages respond to lentinan and, in turn, stimulate lymphocytes and other immune cell defenses. Lentinan is a protein-free polysaccharide, in comparison to flammulin, a protein-rich polysaccharide found in Enoki (*Flammulina velutipes*). Yap et al. (2002) found that lentinan is orally active, and suggests its use as a vaccine in the prevention of tumor development. Sia, G.M. & J.K. Candlish (1999) found that a shiitake extract enhanced the production of normal white blood cells, leading to phagocystosis.

Possible Immune Action of Lentinan Isolated from Shiitake, *Lentinula edodes*

(adapted from a diagram originally featured in
Food Review International, vol.II, no. 1, ed. T. Muzano, 1995)

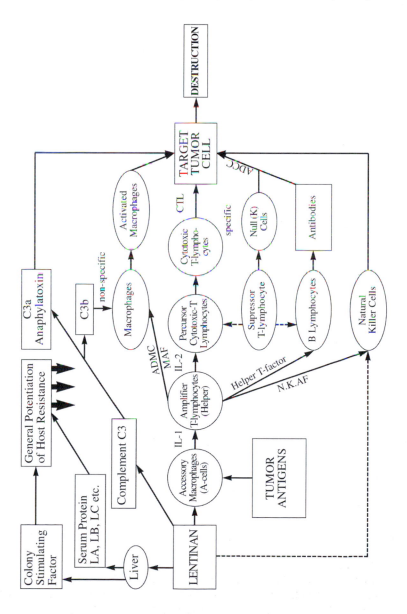

The extract of mushroom mycelium, "LEM" (*Lentinula edodes* mycelium) is an orally active, protein-bound polysac-charide. A water soluble, lignin rich fraction from LEM (JLS-18) has been found to have 70 times the antiviral activity than LEM *in vitro*, and activated NK, T cells, macrophages, and interleukin 6 (Yamamoto et al. 1997). Both have strong anti-tumor properties. In a recent study by Ghoneum at Drew Uni-versity, 11 cancer patients with advanced malignancies were treated with active hemicellulose-compound and showed sig-nificant improvement. Ghoneum (1995) found that arabinoxylanes, derived from the fermentation of rice by shiitake, turkey tail (*Trametes versicolor*) and the split-gill mushroom (*Schizophyllum commune*) increased human NK activity by a factor of 5 in two months. Arabinoxylanes are an enzymatic consequence of the digestion of rice by living myce-lium. Arabinoxylanes, which are composed of xylose and arbinose sugars, have diverse medical benefits. (Hawkins, 2001; Mondoa & Kitei, 2001). Arabinoxylanes from mushroom fer-mented rice also have anti-viral effects (Ghoneum, 1995, 1998).

Other sources of anti-virals from Shiitake have been well docu-mented. An extract from Shiitake mycelium has been shown to be effective against type 1 herpes simplex virus (Sarkar et al., 1993). A water-soluble lignin derivative limited HIV replication *in vitro* and stimulated the proliferation of bone-marrow cells (Suzuki et al., 1990). Clinical trials with lentinan in the treatment of HIV patients showed inhibitory activity (Gordon et al., 1998). However, Abrams (2002) found no sig-nificant advantage in us-ing lentinan in treating AIDs patients. A serine proteinase inhibi-tor has been recently isolated from the fruitbodies of Shiitake (Odani et al., 1999). This mush-room has also been suggested for the treatment of Chronic Fatigue Syndrome (CFS) (Aoki et al., 1987) and as an overall tonic. Anti-bacterial properties have been examined (Hirasawa et al., 1999) and in one study lentinan was shown to be effective at preventing septic shock (Tsujinaka et al., 1990). Hatvani (2001) found that the cell-free extracts from the liquid fermen-tation of mycelium significantly inhibited the growth of the yeast *Candida albicans*, and the bacteria *Strepto-coccus pyogenes*, *Staphylococcus aureus*, and *Bacillus megaterium*. This species is likely to have broad anti-bacterial properties as cultivators have long noted that shiitake are less likely to spoil than most fleshy species grown under the same conditions.

Shiitake mushrooms remain in the vanguard of medicinal mush-rooms. They are relatively inexpensive compared to many other species. Their safety is also well established given the popularity of this culinary mushroom.

Pleurotus ostreatus (Jacquin ex Fries) Kummer

Common Names
Oyster Mushrooms, Hiratake, Tomogitake

Distribution and Natural Habitat
One of the most common of all saprophytic mushrooms, distributed throughout the temperate and tropical forests of the world. Growing saprophytically on broad-leaf hardwoods, sometimes conifers in the spring and fall, especially cottonwood, oak, alder, maple, aspen, ash, beech, birch, elm, willow and poplar.

Known Active Constituents
3-Hydroxy-3-methylglutaryl-coenzyme A reductase
Pleurotus ubiquitin-like protein
Pleuran (ß-glucan)

Form Used
Mushrooms
Mycelium on grain
Fermented mycelium

Medicinal Properties
Recent studies (Gunde-Cimerman et al. 1995, 1999; Bobek et al., 1998) show that *Pleurotus ostreatus* and other closely related species naturally produce a form of Lovastatin® (3-hydroxy-3-methylglutaryl-coenzyme A reductase), a drug approved by the FDA in 1987 for treating excessive blood cholesterol. More Lovastatin® -like constituents are present in the caps than in the stems, more concentrated on the mature gills, and especially in the spores. One model showed that plasma cholesterol turnover was significantly enhanced by 50% with a corresponding 25% decrease in the liver compared to the controls (Bobek et al., 1995). Oyster mushrooms accelerated plasma turnover of cholesterol, resulting in an overall reduction over base lines. This family of compounds may explain the often-

reported cholesterol-reducing effects of many woodland mushrooms (Bobek et al. 1998, 1999).

When mice were implanted with Sarcoma 180 and Oyster mushrooms constituted 20% of their daily diet; the tumors were inhibited by more than 60% after one month compared to the controls (Ying, 1987). In another study, when rats were fed a diet composed of 5% Oyster mushrooms, and administered dimethylhydrazines to induce tumors, fewer formed than the controls. In this study, Zusman et al. (1997) found that when rats were given corncobs 15% colonized by Oyster mushrooms, they were significantly protected from treatment with chemicals which otherwise induced colon cancer, reducing incidence from 47% to 26%. Corncobs without mycelium provided no protection. A lectin from the fruitbodies of Oyster mushrooms, injected into mice, showed potent activity against implanted tumors of Sarcoma 180 and hepatoma H-22. Bobek, P. & S. Galbavy, 2001 have identified a novel beta-glucan, pleuran, which has anti-oxidant effects and may be useful for preventing cancers from metastasizing.

Wang & Ng (2000) first identified a novel, ubiquitin-like protein from Oyster mushrooms that inhibits the HIV-1 reverse transcriptase activity, causing cleavage of transfer RNA. This unique form of ubiquitin appears to govern cell division, inhibiting cells that are infected with HIV. Piraino & Brandt (1999) have also identified a ubiquitin useful as an anti-viral.

Comments

This most common of saprophytic fungi has some promising, newly discovered compounds recommending further investigations. This mushroom is one of the most aggressive of all cultivated mushrooms, and one of the easiest to grow. The spores of this mushroom can cause allergic reactions in some people (Kamm et al.,1991; Horner et al., 1993). Reactions are more likely to occur from older, heavily sporulated mushrooms, which sometimes can host bacteria, which produce negative effects. Oyster mushroom cultivators, if not consistently using filtration masks, can develop allergies to spores over time. For more information, see my book, *Growing Gourmet & Medicinal Mushrooms*, Ten Speed Press, Berkeley.

Insect Parasitizing Mushrooms

Cordyceps sinensis   (Berk.) Sacc.

= *Sphaeria sinensis* Berk.

Common Names
Caterpillar Fungus, Tochukaso, Dong Chong Xia Cao ("Summer Grass, Winter Worm"), Chongcao, Yertsa Gonbu

Distribution and Natural Habitat
Parasitizing the larvae of a caterpillar from a Lepidoptera moth (*Hepialus armoricanus* Oberthur), this mushroom is native to Tibet, and southern China, found in the mountainous meadow regions, growing most commonly in grasslands from 10,000-12,000 ft. in elevation.

Note: *Cordyceps sp.* pictured is not *C. sinensis.*

Known Active Constituents
Cordycepin
Cordycepic acid (mannose)
Galactomannans
Polysaccharides
Sterols

Form Used
Wild collected fruiting bodies on caterpillar larvae
Mycelia grown on grains (primarily rice and soybeans)
Mycelia in liquid fermentation

Medicinal Properties
Antitumor activity and immune stimulant (Tsunoo et al. 1995, et al., 1990; Zhou et al., 1990; Yoshida et al., 1989; Wang & Shiao, 2000). Compounds other than polysaccharides and cordycepin have tumor-inhibiting agents (Kuo et al., 1994). Studies have independently confirmed that *Cordyceps sinensis*

substantially inhibits the proliferation of human leukemia cells *in vitro* (Chen et al., 1997). Liu et al. (1992) also suggested that *C. sinensis* could be used in the treatment of adult leukemia. A study by Kodama et al. (2000) suggests that anti-leukemic activity is targeted towards TdT+ (terminal deoxynucleotidyl transferase-positive) cells, and is enhanced in the presence of an adenosine deaminase inhibitor, supporting the results of a similar study by Koc et al. (1996) which showed that cordycepin was specifically cytotoxic against the same type of leukemia cells. In 2002, the U.S. National Institute of Health began Phase I initial screening of cordycepin, a mannose-based sugar, from the company Oxigene, from *C. sinensis*, as a possible treatment for leukemia.

Ethanol-soluble crude fractions showed activity in enhancing the activity of human NK cells (Xu et al. 1992). Of interest to medical scientists is that this species can both enhance activity of NK cells while at the same time modulate the overproduction of human leukocytes. Koh et al. (2002) showed that the oral ingestion to mice of water extracts of the mycelium of *Cordyceps sinensis* essentially doubled macrophages. A study, as yet unpublished at the time of this writing, by Ohtomo (2002) with cancer cells co-cultured with human spleen cells, showed a doubling of natural killer cells, and up to 40 times more macrophage production when extracts from the cultures of *C. sinensis* mycelium grown on rice were introduced.

Cordyceps also has cholesterol-reducing and general cardiotonic properties (Tsunoo, et al. 1995). Yamaguchi et al. (2000) found that water-soluble extracts of *Cordyceps sinensis* inhibited cholesterol deposition in the aorta by inhibiting LDL oxidation. At an international mycological conference, a group of Japanese researchers presented a paper showing that aqueous extracts of this mushroom dilated the aorta by 40% under stress (Naoki, et al., 1994). The increase in blood flow would benefit muscles pushed to their maximum, thus greatly enhancing endurance. Chiou et al. (2000) found that a crude phosphate-buffered saline extract induced vaso-relaxation. In mouse stress test experiments, Dai et al (2001) suggest that ingestion of products made by *Cordyceps sinensis* mycelium alleviates fatigue and improves physical endurance. Furthermore, hot-water extracts of this fungus have compounds that relax the bronchial passages, loosening bronchoalveolar lavage fluids allowing for a productive cough, facilitating respiration, and is suggested as a treatment for asthma and lung inflammation (Kuo et al. 2001). A clinical study with sexually dysfunctional/impaired men found that 64% improved in performance from ingesting one gram per day (Yang et al., 1985).

In a clinical study of 36 patients with advanced breast and lung cancer, *Cordyceps sinensis* restored immunological function (Zhou & Lin, 1995). Bao et al. (1994) reported that *C. sinensis* helped prevent kidney disease by ameliorating aminoglycoside nephrotoxicity in elderly patients. This species has been further implicated as a liver-fortifier by improving hepatic function and was shown to have a short-term curative effect on hepatitis B in a clinical study of 33 patients (Zhou et al., 1990). A controlled clinical study by Liu et al. (1996) with 80 patients with a Chinese formula that included Cordyceps had a beneficial effect in treating post-hepatitic cirrhosis. Dai et al. (2001) confirmed that liver metabolism improved in rats given a heat-treated mycelial-based *Cordyceps sinensis* product. Li et al. (1996) found that *Cordyceps sinensis* prevented aminoglycoside nephrotoxicity induced by gentamicin in rats.

Antioxidant activities from cultured mycelium are equal to or greater than that from the natural form. Partially purified polysaccharide fractions increased anti-oxidant activities by a factor of 10-30 times, suggesting that these fractions are the source of the anti-oxidants (Li et al., 2001). Anti-viral activity has been reported from China, for helping patients with chronic viral hepatitis, helping 80% of the 256 cases in a clinical study, and is suggested for the efficacious treatment of Lyme disease.

Comments

Known from China for nearly two millennia as an aphrodisiac, the first written record appeared in 200 A.D. in Pents'ao herbal—*Sheng Nung Pents'ao Ching—The Classic Herbal of the Divine Plowman* (Davis, 1983). The sudden growth of this fungus on the cadavers of larvae was viewed as magical by the Chinese, and was thought to impart immortality to the dead. Stone effigies of the infected insects were traditionally used in funeral ceremonies, and placed with the deceased, to represent re-birth of life after death.

Also well known as a treatment for asthma and consumption, for protecting the lungs and kidneys, and for facilitating the flow of phlegm in the windpipe, allowing for discharge of excess fluids from the lungs and windpipe (Gee, 1918). Here is another example whereby traditional use of mushrooms has been confirmed by modern science (Kuo et al. 2001).

First described by the Rev. M.J. Berkeley as *Sphaeria sinensis* (Berk. in 1843), *Cordyceps sinensis* is a parasite on moth larvae (*Lepidoptera* species, primarily *Hepialus armoricanus*) and is native to the high altitude grasslands of the Himalayas (Zhang et al. 1997). The spores of Cordyceps infect silkworm larvae with the resulting mycelium invading the body, killing the host, and then producing a dark, club-like mushroom from the back of its head.

Many mycologists harbor concerns about consuming whole *Cordyceps* mushrooms imported from Asia. Furthermore, I hesitate to recommend eating the natural form, as many other contaminant organisms (molds & bacteria) are associated with the dead and decaying carcass of the larva. At least one report has shown that imported fruitbodies of *Cordyceps* have been contaminated with lead wires (Wu et al., 1996), leading to severe poisoning.

The *in vitro* production of *Cordyceps sinensis* mycelium *sans* caterpillar affords a product of greater consistency, equal or greater potency, and quality assurance (Li et al., 2001). Imported *Cordyceps* can be from a wide variety of strains, varying in potency, and are often fumigated with fungicides to prevent further decay. Mycelial products are generally better than ones generated from fruitbodies. Comparing the natural form versus the mycelium for the production of anti-oxidants Li et al. (2001) found similar levels of anti-oxidant activity. However, water extracts of the mycelial form allowed for a 10-30-fold increase in potency over baselines.

The benefits of *Cordyceps* come from a constellation of compounds, other than polysaccharides, many of which have not yet been identified, but have been and continue to be the subject of scientific studies (Bok et al., 1999; Kuo et al. 1994). One study (Kuo et al., 1996) has shown that two methanol soluble fractions demonstrated immunosuppressive properties while simultaneously providing antitumor effects. Most studies have shown immunoenhancing properties from both crude and purified fractions from *Cordyceps*. One difference may be that the Kuo (1996) study was based on dried, naturally collected cadavers of caterpillar larvae whereas the other studies have been primarily based on extracts from pure cultured mycelia. As noted, the cadavers of caterpillar larvae are resplendent with a multitude of other microorganisms, complicating interpretations from studies using natural forms.

Several imperfect forms of *Cordyceps* have been proposed which raise important questions about the quality of research of the systematics centering on this fungus. The primary mycelium has been called *Paecilomyces hepiali* while other isolates have been given names as new species, i.e. *Mortierella hepiali*, *Scytalidium hepiali* and *Tolypocladimin sinensis* (Zhu et al., 1998, Halpern, 1999). For a single mushroom species to have four imperfect forms is unprecedented and calls into question the validity of such names, and also underscores the difficulty of isolating a pure strain of *Cordyceps sinensis* from the wild. The works of Chen et al., (1999, 2001) show that speciation in this group is complicated and that several closely related but distinct taxa are involved in what is commonly called '*Cordyceps sinensis.*' Currently isolates from the wild, especially originating from those not skilled in the art, may be misnamed. As some *Cordyceps* species and strains are immunosuppresants, such a mistake in identification could be medically dangerous. In the rush to market, vendors and those not skilled in fungal tissue culture and taxonomy are capable of propagating a contaminant and mistake it for *C. sinensis*, passing it on to unsuspecting consumers. A standard for *Cordyceps sinensis* has yet to be established.

This mushroom has made international sports headlines. At the Chinese National Games in 1993, a team of nine Chinese women runners shattered 9 world records, breaking the record for the 10,000 meter run by an unprecedented 42 seconds. They gave credit to their intense training regimen and the use of Cordyceps (Steinkraus 1994; Pegler et al. 1994). Hiyoshi et al., (1996) conducted a limited study on the use of *C. sinensis* mycelium-products on long distance runners, resulting in significant improvement in 71% of the subjects, due, in part, to increased respiratory activity and the metabolism of lactic acid. Recently a marathon runner called me to report that he was able to cut 25 minutes off his time in the Boston Marathon using this mushroom in a tea, placing in the top ten. He did not want his name to be used for fear officials would invalidate his time. Nevertheless, he and other runners continue to incorporate Cordyceps as a component in their training regimens.

Although *Cordyceps sinensis* is best known, hundreds of other species in this genus have yet to be surveyed. Other Cordyceps species are increasingly drawing the attention of the medical establishment, with some surprises. *Cordyceps subsellis* was discovered by Hodge (1996) to be the perfect stage of *Tolypocladium inflatum*, the fungus responsible for the organ-rejection transplant drug, cyclosporin. As a billion dollar industry centers on the production of cyclosporin, her discovery is remarkable, as no others had realized that the mold became a mushroom when it infected an insect host. This event is another wake-up call to the pharmaceutical industry and the medical community that mushrooms can be a valuable and rich source for potent medicines. Two other species worthy of note are *Cordyceps militaris* and *Cordyceps capitata*. At present, mycologists suggest that the genus numbers well over 400 species.

More than 33 species are alpine dwellers and *C. sinensis* is considered rare amongst them. Only an expert specialized in the taxonomy of Cordyceps can correctly identify a collection to species (Zang & Kinjo, 1998).

Cordyceps is a medicinal mushroom preferred by both men and women of all age groups. Its widespread activities as a health tonic—a cardiovascular agent, an immunopotentiator, and a liver fortifer—places Cordyceps in the forefront. I also believe Cordyceps may be useful for the treatment of depression. With increased blood flow to the brain, cognitive and emotional health should improve. Indeed, Cordyceps may be helpful to alleviating many of the problems associated with aging and progressively poorer circulation.

For further reading, I recommend Wang & Shiao (2000) and two books: *Cordyceps: Tonic Food of Ancient China* by Kenneth Jones (Sylvan Press, 1997) and *Cordyceps: China's Healing Mushroom* by Georges M. Halpern, MD (Avery Publishing Group, 1999).

Natural form of *Cordyceps sinensis* growing from caterpillar larvae.

Commonly Asked Questions

1. Who recommends medicinal mushrooms?

Robert C. Atkins, MD

Robert Barnett, Author & Nutritionist
in *Sugars That Heal*, Harper Collins, New York

Brian Becker, M.D., Clinical Lecturer, Program in
Integrative Medicine at the University of Arizona

Harriet Beinfeld
co-author of *Between Heaven and Earth: A Guide to
Chinese Medicine*, Ballatine Books, New York

John Boik
in *Cancer & Natural Medicine: A Textbook of Basic
Science and Clinical Research*, Oregon Medical
Press, Princeton, Minnesota

Francis Brinker, MD
in *Herb Contraindications and Drug Interactions*
Eclectic Institute, Sandy, Oregon

Morton Broffman, PhD
in *Townsend Letter for Doctors & Patients*

Etienne Callebout, MD
in *An Alternative Medicine Definitive Guide to Cancer*,
Future Medicine Publishing, Inc., Tiburon, California

Goro Chihara, PhD
Teikyo University, Nogawa, Japan

W. Lee Cowden, MD
Conservative Medical Institute, Richardson, Texas

Subhuti Dharmananda, PhD
Chinese Herbal Therapies for Immune Disorders,
Eastwind Books, San Francisco, California

W. John Diamond, MD
Medical Director, Triad Medical Center, Reno, Nevada

Patrick Donovan, ND
University Health Clinic, Seattle, Washington

James Duke, PhD
Economic & Medical Botanist (ret.), USDA

Daniel Gagnon, Medical Herbalist
President of Herbs, Etc., Santa Fe, New Mexico

M. Ghoneum, PhD
Drew University of Medicine and Science, Los Angeles

Christopher Hobbs, Herbalist
in *Medicinal Mushrooms*, Botanica Press, Santa Cruz, CA
Tetsuro Ikekawa, PhD
National Cancer Center, Tokyo, Japan
Chris Kilham, faculty U Mass/Amherst, and author of
Psyche Delicacies and *Tales from the Medicine Trail*
Jan Lelley, PhD
author of *Die Heilkraft de Pilze: Gesund durch
Mykotherapie*
Takashi Mizuno, PhD.,
Professor Emeritus, Shizuoka University, Japan
Emil I. Mondoa, MD & **Mindy Kitei**, 2001,
authors of *Sugars That Heal: The New Healing Science
of Glyconutrients*. Ballantine Publishing Group, NY
Michael Murray, ND & **Joseph Pizzorno**, ND
in *The Encyclopedia of Natural Medicines*,
MacDonald & Co., Ltd., London
Hiroaki Nanba, PhD
Kobe Pharmaceutical University, Japan
Robert C. Rountree, MD
Helios Health Center, Boulder, Colorado
Richard Sarnat, MD, **Paul Schulick** and **Tom Newmark**
authors of *The Life Bridge*, Herbal Free Press, Vermont
John E. Smith, BSc, MSc, PhD, DSc, FIBiol, FRSE,
Emeritus Professor of Applied Microbiology, U. of Strathclyde
Jesse Stoff, MD
Solstice Clinical Associates, Tucson, Arizona
Earl Surwit, MD,
Clinical Professor of Obstetrics, Gynecology, and Surgery,
University of Arizona, Director of Gynecological Oncology
of Arizona Oncology Associates, and Co-Founder of
Sunstone Healing Center, a not-for-profit cancer support
foundation, <http://www.sunstonehealing.net/
Jack Taylor, DC
Dr. Taylor's Wellness Center, Rolling Meadows, Illinois
Ron Teeguarden, Herbalist
in *Chinese Tonic Herbs*, Japan Publications, Tokyo
Leslie Tierra, Herbalist
in *The Herbs of Life*, Crossing Press, Freedom, CA
Michael Tierra, Herbalist
in *The Way of Herbs*, Simon & Schuster, New York

Susan Weed
in *Breast Cancer, Breast Health*, Ashtree Press,
Woodstock, New York
Andrew Weil, MD
Director of the Program for Integrative Medicine,
University of Arizona Medical School, Tucson, Arizona
Terry Willard, PhD
Director, Wild Rose College, Calgary, Alberta, Canada

2. Why water/alcohol extracts?

Most of the active polysaccharides of mushrooms are soluble
in water, but some are miscible in alcohols. When alcohol is
added and becomes greater than 25+%, the water-soluble
polysaccharides precipitate. Some of the active polysaccharides and their haptenes are soluble in alcohol, but insoluble in
water, as in the case of *Agaricus blazei* (Kawagishi et al. 1988).
The ethanol precipitate from the mycelium of *A. blazei* has
been found by Sorimachi et al. (2001) to induce interleukin-8
from macrophages and tumor necrosis factors. Recent work
by Ooi et al. (2002) showed that a hot water extraction of Reishi
mushrooms precipitated in ethanol strongly inhibited the growth
of Sarcoma 180 in *vivo*. Shi et al. (2002) determined that hot-
water extracts from Reishi mushrooms afforded a
genoprotective effect on DNA, preventing chromosomal damage from oxidizing free radicals. Wang & Shiao (2000) report
on the positive efficacy of studies using alcohol extracts of
Cordyceps sinensis mycelium, as well as water extracts. These
studies and numerous others underscore that both water and
alcohol fractions contain medicinally important compounds.
Mushroom products containing both the water and alcohol
extractions give you two shields of protection. Alcohol also
acts as a natural preservative, preventing the souring of the
protein-rich polysaccharides from microorganisms.

3. Why is it important that mushrooms be grown organically?

Mushrooms are great sources of medicines but they can also
concentrate heavy metals, especially if their culture is proxi-
mate to an industrialized area (Wu et al., 1996; Byrne, 1995;
Stijve, 1977, 1984, 1990, 1991, 1992; Kawamura et al., 1991;
Muramatsu et al. 1991). Pollutants from air and water can be
taken up from the soil and passed directly into the mycelial
network. It is essential that not only mushrooms are grown

according to certified organic practices, but are grown in environments free of air and water pollution. Remember: mushrooms are a reflection of the environment in which they are grown.

Simple questions to ask your supplier: Where are their mushrooms grown? Do you provide an analysis for pesticide residues? Answers to these questions could significantly influence the quality of medicinal properties of the mushroom products being marketed and consumed.

4. Which medicinal mushroom is the best for treatment of cancer?

First, of course, consult an oncologist and/or a qualified medical practitioner. This is a tough question, since cancers vary so much. Given that only a few clinical studies have been completed, it is difficult to give specific answers at this time. However, we do know that several unique polysaccharides individually awaken the immune system, and several mushrooms possess compounds that are anti-tumorigenic per se (Fujimoto et al., 1984, 1991; Nakazato et al., 1994; Sugimachi et al., 1997). Ghoneum et al. (1995, 1998, 1999) reported that a concoction of multiple mushroom species induced a pronounced immune response. An as yet unpublished study by Ohtomo (2002) shows pronounced enhancement of macrophage and natural killer cell activity, from the extracts of mycelium grown on rice, increasing several-fold natural killer cells macrophages and interleukins. Furthermore, the combination of 7 species provided for a better immunological response than any one species at the same, comparative dose. Hence, if I were the patient, I would consult a qualified medical practitioner to explore the use of a multiple-mushroom blend to maximize immune response. See descriptions of each species for specific activities, scientific reports and/or clinical studies for different types of cancer.

5. Are these extracts good as a preventative to disease, including cancers?

From the information gathered thus far, yes. See, for example, Ikekawa (1989), and the references cited in Question 4.

6. For those undergoing chemotherapy or radiation therapy, are medicinal mushroom products useful?

Yes. Many of the clinical studies show positive benefits with patients who have undergone radiation and chemotherapy in the treatment of cancers (Nakazato et al. 1994). A number of mushroom species have demonstrated a protective and regenerative effect on cells exposed to radiation and chemotherapy, including Maitake, Reishi, Zhu Ling, Suehirotake, and Yun Zhi (Fujimoto et al., 1984; Chang & But, 1986; Kobayashi et al., 1993; Fujimoto et al., 1991, Kim et al, 1999; Kim et al., 1999; Sugimachi et al., 1997; Namba, 1997; Kimura et al., 1994). In one case study with advanced breast cancer (Wedam & Haynes, 1997), complete recovery was accomplished after a regimen of chemotherapy and alternative therapies incorporating the daily consumption of a 4-mushroom tea blend. Several studies have confirmed that a multiple-species approach has had a dramatic effect on increasing natural killer (NK) cell activity, extending the lifespans of the patients suffering from a variety of cancers (Ghoneum 1995, 1998). Fairly large human clinical studies (Fujimoto et al., 1991; Miyazaki et al., 1995) show positive increases in survival factors when using a derivation of Suehirotake, the Split Gill Polypore (*Schizophyllum commune*). Modern testing protocols have similarly indicated that a multiple mushroom approach affords a better immune response than a single mushroom (Ohtomo, 2002).

7. What is Maitake "D-fraction"?

The delta fraction of Maitake, coined "D-fraction," describes a derivative of a high-molecular-weight polysaccharide (1,000,000 m.w.) that is acid-insoluble, alkali-soluble, and hot water extractable. The fraction is composed of 1,6 beta-glucans carrying 1,3 branches. All fruitbodies of Maitake contain this fraction. Maitake Corporation of Parasmus, New Jersey has trademarked the phrase Maitake D-fraction®, although the phrase was widely in circulation prior to trademark approval. One report (Shigeuse et al. 2000) expressed concern that when mice were immunized with a "D-fraction" of Maitake arthritic-like symptoms developed. This report—of an isolated constituent—is contrary to those seen in studies with whole mushrooms such as Reishi, and the uses of mushrooms in traditional Chinese and European medicine for the treatment of arthritis.

8. Why not produce a highly purified extract of, for instance, Maitake to isolate the delta fraction from Maitake?

Several studies suggest that the high and mid-range molecular-weight polysaccharides have greater stimulatory effects than any one of its isolated constituents. Adachi et al (1990) found that there was greater immunological benefit from a heat-treated 'mother' polysaccharide (800,000+ m.w.) than from the isolated, derivative polysaccharides of lower molecular weights of 250,000, 21,000, and 6400. Mizuno (1995, pp. 32–33) and Broffman (1997) also underscored the importance of constituents other than (1-3)-ß-D-glucans, and suggested that other components within the mushrooms helped increase activity. The following model is suggested: the human immune system is empowered by the decomposition of coarse polysaccharides into synergistic subcomponents, whose pathways lead to activation of effector sites, thus sensitizing immunological responses. In essence, this effect may be summarized by the adage that "the whole is greater than the sum of its parts." Hence, a crude extract from multiple mushrooms is, in my opinion, better than any one isolated, purified constituent from a single species. When examining the voluminous scientific literature on medicinal mushrooms, it is clear that the number of active, beneficial constituents far supercedes that of one active constituent.

9. Why use a mushroom blend?

A number of researchers (Ghoneum et al., 1995, 1998) have come to the conclusion that, to maximize a host-mediated response—that is, to 'awaken' the immune system—a panoply of polysaccharides and medicinal mushroom constituents is best. These constituents increase the number and activity of macrophages, killer T and NK (natural killer) lymphocytes. Combining medicinal mushroom species sends the immune system multiple stimuli, awakening the body's natural defenses. As each species is a unique combination of these macro-sugars, their decomposition sequences result in sub-derivatives that are unique, activating a broader spectrum of receptor sites in the immune system than from just one species or compound (Ohtomo et al. 2002). One recent case study utilizing four of our medicinal mushrooms resulted in complete recovery from breast cancer. The patient combined allopathic and naturopathic treatments (Wedam & Haynes, 1997).

Not only are there medicinal polysaccharides in mushrooms, but also a wide variety of other constituents may help improve human health. Many species have direct tumor-growth-inhibiting effects with no or little cytotoxicity to healthy cells, an extraordinary characteristic of any cancer therapy. The LD50, an inverse measurement of toxicity illustrating the dose lethal to 50% of a population of organisms, is typically extraordinarily high in these medicinal mushrooms, meaning they have very low toxicity, several orders of magnitude lower than most antibiotics or other immunostimulants.

Cordyceps is thought to extend the longevity of healthy cells, increase blood flow, and lower cholesterol levels. Several species improves liver and/or kidney function. There are recent reports that compounds in Lion's Mane mushrooms (*Hericium erinaceus*) may stimulate nerve regeneration. Although, we are still just exploring their potential medical uses, researchers worldwide have come to the same conclusion. Mushrooms are powerful natural medicines—especially for those challenged by stress-related disease complexes. Hence, a blend of medicinal fungi can offer a powerful therapeutic punch.

10. If I have a yeast (*Candida albicans*) infection, should I ingest medicinal mushrooms?

The scientific literature abounds with references showing that the metabolites of mushrooms produce natural antibiotics that fight *Candida albicans*. (Tsukagoshi et al. 1984;; Sakagami et al. 1991; Suay et al. 2000). Oh et al., 1998 found that the protein-bound polysaccharides from *Ganoderma lucidum* activated macrophage activity, enhancing the elimination of *Candida albicans*. Since so many of the medicinal mushrooms enhance macrophage activities, a similar response is to be expected. In nature, mushroom mycelium uses yeasts as a food source. Hence the addition of yeast to the culture media, before sterilization, is common as yeast provides essential vitamins and nutrients, helping the mycelium grow. So, the answer to this commonly asked question is "yes."

11. Should mushrooms be cooked?

Mushrooms should be cooked before being eaten. They offer little nutritional or medicinal benefit if not heat tenderized. Experts in nutrition like Andrew Weil, and numerous experts in mycology agree. Cell wall constituents such as, but not limited to, protein-bound polysaccharides are not readily digestible without heat treatment. It is well known that, for instance, raw shiitake mushrooms will pass undigested if uncooked, whereas they will be digested when subjected to heat. This is because the polysaccharides are in a matrix of chitinous-like cells forming the tough exoskeleton of the mycelium. (The mycelium that the Ice Man had survived 5300 years intact!) Compacted mycelium makes a mushroom, with additional differentiation arising at the end of the life cycle, and in doing so further differentiation of constituents occur. Hence, fuzzy mycelium can articulate into a beautiful mushroom, and when you clone that mushroom, it regenerates into the same mycelium from which it sprung. So if you want to maximize the benefits from ingesting medicinal mushrooms, make sure they are heat tempered first. Furthermore, although there are excellent clinical studies on the positive effects of, for instance, Suehirotake, the Split Gill Polypore, *Schizophyllan commune*, this mushroom can cause lung and brain infection and inflammation if presented in an unheated form to those with compromised immune systems. To not cook this mushroom would mean the consumer would be exposed to a potentially dangerously infectious agent.

12. If these mushrooms stimulate the immune system, and they promote interleukins, how can they be anti-inflammatory?

Whole mushrooms and grain-grown mycelium enhance the immune system and are known as biological response modifiers. Medicinal mushrooms such as Reishi promote immune response to antigens through the production of cytokines and interleukins from polysaccharides but do not result in an over-excitation, modulating immune response, and can be anti-inflammatory (Ukai et al., 1983: Ooi & Liu, 1999). As Reishi and other mushrooms stimulate the cellular expression of super-oxide dismutase that scavenge free radicals, medicinal mushrooms have the unique effect of increasing macrophage production while reducing collateral damage to healthy tissue. (Lin et al., 1995; Zhou & Gao, 2002; Small et al., 2000; Lee et al. 2001). The respiratory expression of nitric oxide from the macrophages plays an important role in modulating inflammation and immune response (Lowenstein & Snyder, 1992). Steroidal components—lanostanic triterpenoids within this mushroom—also have a mitigating influence in suppressing inflammatory factors while the immune system is activated (Stavinoha et al., 1990, 1996; Stavinoha 1997).

13. "Every published, independent study on the use of medicinal mushrooms for immune health has been conducted with a hot water or hot water/alcohol extract."

Not true. Although many of the articles in the scientific literature discuss fractionation sequences using hot water, ethanol, methanol and other solvents, particularly for polysaccharides, and this has been the traditional method, new delivery systems have proven equal or greater efficacy. Studies by Ghoneum (1994, 1995, 1996, 1998) Matsui et al. (1998) and Ohtomo (2002) show that heat-treated mycelium grown on sterilized rice provides an easily digestible arabinoxylane complex with strong immunomodulatory activity. Surprising to many is that immunological activity of this combination is high, comparatively, although beta glucan content can be very low. Enzymes secreted by the mycelium convert glucose and other sugars in rice into arabinoxylanes and glycoproteins, while the mycelium manufactures polysaccharides, ergosterols (Provitamin D), triterpenoids, fiber and other compounds.

Live mycelial extracts offer a unique advantage as an antimicrobial tonic. In so far as antimicrobial, including anti-viral compounds, are destroyed by heat, the natural antibiotics from mushroom mycelia are preserved through low temperature extraction. Cervical cancer, liver cancer, some forms of gastrointestinal cancers, and others may be caused by viruses, or stimulated by the activities of microbes. Many of these microbes are inhibited from the extracellular, natural antibiotics secreted from the living mushroom mycelia (Anke et al., 1989; Suay et al., 2000; Stamets, 2001a, 2002). As with most antibiotics, they are better preserved through live fermentation extraction at low temperatures than from high heat.

Mushrooms provide a diversified immunological shield from a pantheon of diseases and disease organisms. Fractionation removes many of benefits diverse mushroom products provide for host defense. The interactions on immune health are complex. Mushroom medicine is a rich field with hundreds, perhaps thousands of active constituents. We are just beginning to understand how to orchestrate their forms for optimum medical benefit.

14. When taking Cordyceps, is it best to use the natural form (fruitbodies from caterpillar larvae) or mycelium-based products?

Natural forms imported from China are fraught with risks of which most consumers are not aware. When a caterpillar dies from an infection from *Cordyceps sinensis*, many opportunistic molds – Aspergillus, Penicillium, Candida (a yeast), bacteria and protozoa are often also present. When pure mycelium is grown under laboratory conditions, quality is assured. Furthermore, potency is equal or greater than that from wild specimens (Li et al., 2001). Unscrupulous exporters have implanted lead wires into wild Cordyceps to boost the weight (value) of their products, leading to severe lead poisoning in at least two consumers (Wu et al., 1996). This author knows no reports as to how widespread this practice is. Another factor one should consider in buying cultured Cordyceps is the consistency from using one strain. As wild Cordyceps is hand-collected by villagers in China and Tibet, many strains are gathered and then exported, meaning that there can be considerable variation in strains. Furthermore, to prevent invasion from other fungi of the wild Cordyceps post harvest, Chinese herbal vendors in the San Francisco Bay Area have told me that many bundles of wild Cordyceps are treated with fungicides. As with all medicinal mushroom products, buying those that are certified organic from reputable suppliers, ensures the best quality.

15. If I am borderline diabetic, with type II non-insulin dependent diabetes, will mushrooms help?

Obviously, consulting a specialist is recommended. According to Konno et al. (2001) Kubo et al. (1994), and Manohar et al. (2002), diabetics may benefit from better modulation of glucose metabolism.

16. Are there any studies that show that certain mushrooms are safe to take in an extract form during pregnancy and at what dose?

No, none that I know. In absence of precise information to the contrary, I would still error on the side of caution and not recommend the use of extracts during pregnancy. Consult a qualified medical practitioner, which frankly may be difficult to find in this subject field.

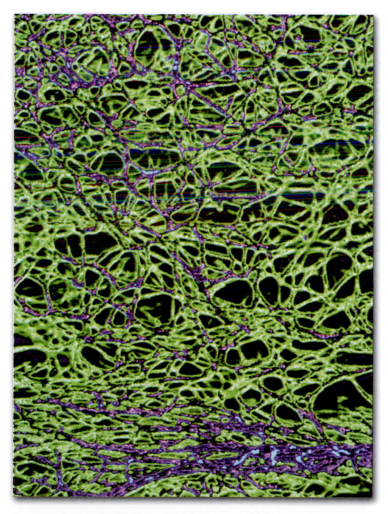

Scanning electron micrograph of mushroom mycelium magnified approximately 500 diameters.

Supporting References

Abrams, D., 2002. Personal communication.

Adachi, Y., N. Ohno, M. Ohsawa, S. Oikawa, & T. Yadomae, 1990. "Change of biological activities of (1—3)-beta-D-glucan from *Grifola frondosa* upon molecular weight reduction by heat treatment" *Chemical and Pharmaceutical Bulletin* 38 (2): 477-81.

Adachi, Y., M. Okazaki, N. Ohno, and T. Yadomae, 1994. "Enhancement of cytokine production by macrophages stimulated with (1—3)-beta-D-glucan, grifolan (GRN), isolated from *Grifola frondosa*. *Biol.Phar. Bull*. Dec; 17(12) 1554-60.

Adachi, K. et al., 1987. "Potentiation of host-mediated antitumor activity in mice by B-glucan obtained from *Grifola frondosa* (Maitake)" *Chemical and Pharmaceutical Bulletin* 35:262-270.

Adachi, et al. 1988. "Blood pressure lowering activity present in the fruitbody of *Grifola frondosa* (Maitake)."*Chemical and Pharmaceutical Bulletin* 3: 1000-1006.

Adachi, Y., N. Ohno, M. Ohsawa, S. Oikawa, T. Yadomae, 1990. "Change of biological activities of (1—3) beta-D-glucan from *Grifola frondosa* upon molecular weight reduction by heat treatment. "*Chemical and Pharmaceutical Bulletin*. Feb; 38:(2):477-481.

Adachi, Y., N. Ohno & T. Yadomae, 1998. "Activation of murine kuppfer cells with gel-forming (1‡3) -beta-D-glucan from *Grifola frondosa*" *Biological and Pharmaceutical Bulletin* Mar; 21(3):278-283.

Akihisa T, Takamine Y, Yoshizumi K, Tokuda H, Kimura Y, Ukiya M, Nakahara T, Yokochi T, Ichiishi E, Nishino H., 2002. Microbial transformations of two lupane-type triterpenes and anti-tumor-promoting effects of the transformation products. *Journal of Natural Products* Mar;65(3):278-82.

Andreacchi, A. 1995. "Characterization of AA 567, a coronary vasodilator and ca-channel antagonist produced by a basidiomycete species YL 8006." Ph.D. Dissertation, University of Rochester, Dept. of Chemical Engineering.

Andreacchi, A., T. Wang & J.H. Wu, 1997. "Cardiovascular effects of the fungal extract of basidiomycetes sp. YL8006" *Life Sciences*, vol. 60, no. 22, pp. 1987-1994.

Anke, T., 1989. "Basidiomycetes: a source of new bioactive secondary metabolites" *Progress in Industrial Microbiology* 27:51-66.

Aoki, T. et al., 1987. "Low natural killer syndrome: Clinical and immunologic features" *Nat. Immun. Cell. Growth Regul*. 6: 116-28.

Aoki, M., T. Motomu, A. Fukushima, T. Hieda, S. Kubo. M. Takabayashi, K. Ono & Y. Mikami, 1993. "Antiviral substances with systemic effects produced by Basidiomycetes such as *Fomes fomentarius*" *Bioscience, Biotechnology & Biochemistry* 57(2): 278-293.

Arika, T., K. Amemiya & S. Mochizuki, 1986. "Combination of radiation and schizophyllan (SPG) in C3H mouse squamous-cell carcinoma" *Gan-T-Kagaku-Ryoho*.Sept; 13(9):2841-7.

Asanoma, M., K. Takahashi, M. Miyabe, K. Yamamoto, N. Yoshimi, H. Mori & Y. Kawazoe, 1994. "Inhibitory effect of topical application of polymerized ferulic acid, a synthetic lignin, on tumor promotion in mouse skin two stage tumorigenesis" *Carcinogenesis* vol. 15, no. 9, pp. 2069-2071.

Atsumi, S., K. Umezawa, H. Iinuma, H. Naganawa, H. Nakamura, Y. Iitaka & T. Takeuchi, 1990. "Production, isolation and structure determination of a novel beta-glucosidase inhibitor, cyclophellitol, from *Phellinus sp*." *Journal of Antibiotics* (Tokyo) Jan;43(1):49-53.

Bankhead, C., 1999. "Mushrooms may play role in breast cancer prevention and treatment" *Medicine Science News* Dec. 10th.

Bau, Z.D., Z.G. Wu, and F. Zheng, 1994. "Amelioration of aminoglycoside nephrotoxicity by *Cordyceps sinensis* in old patients" *Chung-Kuo-Chung-Hsi-I-Chieh-Ho-Tsa-Chih*, May; 14(5): 271-3, 259.

Berkeley, M.J., 1843. "On entomogenous Sphaera" *London Journal of Botany* 2:205-211.

Blanchette, R.A., B.D. Compton, N. J. Turner & R.L. Gilbertson, 1992. "Nineteenth century shaman grave guardians are carved *Fomitopsis officinalis* sporophores" *Mycologia* 84(1):119-24.

Bobek, P., O. Ozdin & M. Mikus, 1995. "Dietary oyster mushroom (*Pleurotus ostreatus*) accelerates plasma cholesterol turnover in hypercholesterolaemic rat" *Physiological Research* 44(5): 287-291.

Bobek, P., L. Ozdin, S. Galbavy, 1998. "Dose and time-dependent hypocholesterolemic effect of oyster mushroom (*Pleurotus ostreatus*) in rats" *Nutrition Mar*; 14(3):282-286.

Bobek, P., E. Ginter, M. Jurcovicova, & L. Kuniak, 1999. "Actual reviews for selected medicinal properties of mushrooms. Cholesterol reducing effect of Pleurotus species (*Agaricomycetidease*) (Abstracts of papers published in 1991-1999)" *International Journal of Medicinal Mushrooms*, vol. 1 pp. 371-380.

Bobek, P. & S. Galbavy, 2001. "Effect of pleuran (beta-glucan from *Pleurotus ostreatus*) on the antioxidant status of the organism and on dimehtylhydrazine-induced pre-cancerous lesions in rat colon" *British Journal of Biomedical Science* 58(3): 164-168.

Bok, J.W., L. Lerner, J. Chilton, H.G. Klingeman, & GHN Tonwers, 1998. "Antitumor sterols from the mycelia of *Cordyceps sinensis*" *Phytochemistry*, July 1999: 891-898.

Brandt, C.R., F. Piraino, 2000. "Mushroom antivirals" *Recent Research Developments for Antimicrobial Agents and Chemotherapy* 4 (2000): 11-26.

Broffman, M. 1997. "Mushrooms as Immune Umbrella for the 21st Century". *Townsend Letter for Doctors and Patients*, October.

Burczk, J., A. Gawron, M. Slotwinska, B. Smietana, and K. Terminisa, 1996. "Antimitotic activity of aqueous extracts of *Inonotus obliquus*" *Boll Chim Farm* May 135:306-309.

Byrne, A., Z. Slejkovec, T. Stijve, L. Fay, W. Gossler, J. Gailers and K.J. Irgolics, 1996. "Arsenobetaine and other arsenic species in mushrooms" *Applied Organometallic Chemistry*, v. 9, 309-313.

Capasso, L., 1998. "5300 years ago, the Ice Man used natural laxatives and antibiotics" *Lancet* 352:1864.

Chairul, S.M. & Y. Hayashi, 1994. "Lanostanoid triterpenes from *Ganoderma applanatum*" *Phytochemistry* 35: 5; 1305-1308.

Chang, Jung-lieh, 1983. "Experimental study of antitumor effect of an extract derived from Zhu-Ling (*Polyporus umbellatus*)" Institute of Material Medica, Academy of Traditional Chinese Medicine, Peking, China.

Chang, H.M. & P.P. But 1986. *Pharmacology and Applications of Chinese Materia Medica*. Vol.1. Singapore, World Scientific.

Chang, H.M. & P.P. But 1987. *Pharmacology and Applications of Chinese Materia Medica*. Vol.1I. Singapore, World Scientific.

Chairul, et al. (1994), Gan et al., (1998) and Ming et al. (2002) discovered novel Ganoderma lanostoids, triterpenes and aldehydes, which have potential medicinal properties.

Chen, K. and W. Zhang, 1987. "Advances in anti-aging herbal medicines in China" *Abstracts of Chinese Medicines* 1: 309-330.

Chen, A. & P. Miles, 1996. "Biomedical research and the application of mushroom nutriceuticals from *Ganoderma lucidum*" in *Mushroom Biology and Mushroom Products*, Penn State University, University Park, Pa.

Chen, A.W., R.B. Cooper, N.L. Huang & S.H. Han, 1998. "*Grifola frondosa* (Maitake): Ecology & Morphology" *Mushroom Grower's Newsletter*, June

Chen, W.C., D.M. Hau, C.C. Wang, I.H. Lin, and S.S. Lee, 1995 "Effects of *Ganoderma lucidum* and krestin on subset T-cell in spleen of gamma-irradiated mice." *American Journal of Chinese Medicine*. American Journal of Chinese Medicine 23(3-4): 289-98.

Chen, Y.J., 1997. "Effect of *Cordyceps sinensis* on the proliferation and differentiation of human leukemic U937 cells." *Life Sciences* 60 (25): 2349-2359.

Chen, Y.J., Y.P. Zhang, Y. Yand & D. Yang, 1999. "Genetic diversity and taxonomic implication of *Cordyceps sinensis* as revealed by RAPD Markers." *Biochemical Genetics* 37: Nos.5/6; 201-213.

Chen, Y.J., N. Wang, L. Qu, T. Li and W. Zang. "Determination of the anamorph of *Cordyceps sinensis* inferred from the analysis of the ribosomal DNA internal transcribed spacers and 5.8s rDNA" *Biochemical Systematics and Ecology* 29: 597-607.

MycoMedicinals: *An Informational Treatise on Mushrooms*

Chihara, G. et al., 1969. Inhibition of mouse sarcoma 180 by polysaccharides from *Lentinus edodes* (Berk.) Sing. *Nature* 222: 637-688.

Chihara, G., 1987. "Antitumor and metastasis-inhibitory activities of lentinan as an immunomodulator: an overview". *Cancer Det. Prev. Suppl.* 1: 423-443.

Chihara, G., 1992. "Immunopharmacology of lentinan, a polysaccharide isolated from *Lentinus edodes*: Its application as a host defense potentiator" *International Journal of Oriental Medicine* 17: 55-77.

Chiou, W.F., P.C. Chang, C.J. Chou & C.F. Chen, 2000. "Protein constituent contributes to hypotensive and vasorelaxant activities of *Cordyceps sinensis*" *Life Sciences* Feb 25; 66(14):1369-76.

Cochran, K.W., 1978. "Medical effects". In *The biology and cultivation of edible mushrooms* by S.T. Chang and W.A. Hayes, eds., Academic Press, New York, pp. 160-187.

Collins, R.A., and T.B. Ng, 1997. "Polysaccharopeptide from *Coriolus versicolor* has potential for use against human immunodeficiency virus type 1 infection" *Life Sciences* 60(25): PL383-7.

Dai, G., T. Bao & R. Cooper, 2001. "CordyMax CS-4 improves steady-state bio-energy status in mouse liver" *Journal of Alternative Complementary Medicine* June; 7(3):231-240.

Davis, W., 1983. "Notes on the Ethnomycology of Boston's China Town" *Harvard Botanical Leaflets* 29:1, p 59-67.

Dong, Y., C.Y. Kwan, S.N. Chen, & M.Yang, 1996. "Antitumor effects of a refined polysaccharide peptide fraction isolated from *Coriolus versicolor*: In Vitro and In Vivo Studies". May, *Research Communications in Molecular Pathology and Pharmacology* vol. 92, No. 2, pp. 140-147.

Dong, Y., M.M. Yang and C.Y. Kwan, 1997. "In vitro inhibition of proliferation of HL-60 cells by tetrandrine and *Coriolus versicolor* peptide derived from Chinese medicinal herbs" *Life Sciences* 60*8): PL135-40.

Duke, J., 1999. Personal communication.

Ebina, T. and K. Murata, 1994. "Antitumor effect of intratumoral administration of a *Coriolus* preparation, PSK: inhibition of tumor invasion in vitro." *Gan To Kagaku Ryoho* 21: 2241-3.

Eo, S.K., Y.S. Kim, C.K. Lee & S.S. Han, 1999. "Antiviral activities of various water and methanol soluble substances isolated from *Ganoderma lucidum*." *Journal of Ethnopharmacology* Dec 15;68(1-3):129-36.

Eo, S.K., Y.S. Kim & C.K. Lee & S.S. Han, 2000. "Possible mode of antiviral activity of acidic protein bound polysaccharide isolated from *Ganoderma lucidum* on herpes simplex viruses." *Journal of Ethnopharmacology* Oct; 72(3): 475-81.

Fujimiya, Y., Y. Suzuki, KI. Oshiman, H. Kobori, K. Moriguchi, H. Nakashima, Y. Matumoto, S.Takahara, T. Ebina, R. Katakura, 1998. "Selective tumoricidal effect of soluble proteoglucan extracted from the basidiomycete, *Agaricus blazei* Murrill, mediated via natural killer cell activation and apoptosis" *Cancer Immunology Immunotherapy* 46:147-159.

Fujimoto, S., H. Furue, T. Kimura, T. Kondo, K. Orita, T. Taguchi, K. Yoshida & N. Ogawa, 1984. "Clinical evaluation of schizophyllan adjuvant immunochemotherapy for patients for respectable gastric cancer – a randomized controlled trial." *Japanese Journal of Surgery* Jul;14(4):286-92.

Fujimoto, S., H. Furue, T. Kimura, T. Kondo, K. Orita, T. Taguchi, K. Yoshida & N. Ogawa, 1991. " Clinical outcome of postoperative adjuvant immunochemotherapy with sizofiran for patients with respectable gastric cancer: a randomized controlled study" *European Journal of Cancer* 27(9):1114-8.

Fukashima, M., T. Ohashi, Y. Fujiwara, K. Sonoyama & M. Nakano 2001. "Cholesterol lowering effects of maitake (*Grifola frondosa*) fiber, shiitake (*Lentinus edodes*) fiber, and Enokitake (*Flammulina velutipes*) fiber in rats. *Exp. Biol. Med.* (Maywood). Sep; 226(8): 758-65.

Fullerton, S.A., A.A. Samadi, D.G. Tortorelis, C. Mallouh & H. Tazaki & S. Kunno,2000. "Apoptosis in Prostatic Cancer Cells with Maitake Mushroom Extract: Potential Alternative Therapy" *Molecular Urology* 4 (1): 7-13.

Furukawa, S., Y. Furukawa, E. Satoyoshi, & K. Hayashi, 1986. "Synthesis and secretion of nerve growth factor by mouse astroglial cells in culture" *Biochemical and Biophysical Research Communications*, vol. 136, no.1, pp. 57-63.

Furusawa, E., S.C. Chou, S. Furusawa, et al. 1992. "Antitumor activity of *Ganoderma lucidum*, an edible mushroom, on intraperitoneally implanted Lewis lung carcinoma in synergenic mice. *Phytotherapy Research* 6: 300-304.

Gan, K.H., S.H. Kuo & C.N. Lin, 1998. "Steroidal constituents of *Ganoderma applanatum* and *Ganoderma neo-japonicum*" *Journal of Natural Products* Nov; 61(11):1421-2.

Gao, X.X., X.F. Fei, B.X. Wang, J. Zhang, Y.J. Gong, M. Minami, T. Nagata, & T. Ikejima, 2000. "Effects of polysaccharides (F10-b) from mycelium of *Ganoderma tsugae* on inflammatory cytokine production by THP-1 cells and human PBMC (I). *Acta Pharmacol Sin* Dec; 21(12):1179-85.

Gao, J.J., B.S. Min, E.M. Ahn, N. Nakamura, H.K. Lee & M. Hattori, 2002. "New triterpenes aldehydes, lucialadehydes A-C, from *Ganoderma lucidum* and their cytotoxicity against murine and human tumor cell lines" *Chemical & Pharmacological Bulletin* Jun; 50(6):837-40.

Garcia-Lora, A., S. Pedrinaci, & F. Garrido, 2001. "Protein bound polysaccharide K and interleukin-2 regulate different nuclear transcription factors in the NKL human natural killer cell line" *Cancer Immunology & Immunotherapy.* June., 50(4):191-198.

Gau, J.P., C.K. Lin, S.S. Lee, and S.R. Lang, 1990. "The lack of antiplatelet effect of crude extracts from *Ganoderma lucidum* on HIV-positive hemophiliacs" *American Journal of Chinese Medicine 18(3-4): 175-9.*

Gee, N.G., 1918. "Notes on *Cordyceps sinensis*" *Mycological Note by C.G. Lloyd* June No. 54 767-768.

Ghoneum, M., 1994. "NK-Immunomodulation by active hemicellulose compound (AHCC) in 17 cancer patients." *Abstract of 2nd Meeting Society of Natural Immunity*, Taormina, Italy, May 25-28.

Ghoneum, M. 1995. "Immunomodulatory and anti-cancer properties of (MGN-3), a modified xylose from rice bran, in 5 patients with breast cancer" Abstract, 87th *Meeting Am. Ass. Cancer Res. (AACR) special conference: "The Interference between Basic and Applied Research"* November 5-8, 1995. Baltimore, MD.

Ghoneum, M., 1998. "Enhancement of human natural killer cell activity by modified arabinoxylane from rice bran (MGM-3)". *International Journal of Immunotherapy* XIV(2) 89-99.

Ghoneum, M., 1998. "Anti-HIV activity in vitro of MGN-3, an activated arabinoxylane from rice bran" *Biohechemical and Biophysical Research Communications* 243: 25-29.

Ghoneum, M. & G. Namatalla, 1996. "Natural killer immunomodulatory function in 27 cancer patients by MGN-3, a modified arabinoxylane from rice bran" *Abstract. Ann. Assoc. Cancer Res.*, April 2-4, 1996, Washington, D.C.

Ghoneum, M., M. Wimbley, F. Salem, A. Mcklain, N. Attallan, G. Gill, 1995. "Immunomodulatory and anticancer effects of active hemicellulose compound (AHCC)." *Int. Journal of Immunotherapy* XI (1): 23-28.

Gordon, M., B. Bihari, E. Goosby, R. Gorter, M. Greco, M. Guralnik, T. Mimura, V. Rudinicki, R. Wong & Y. Kaneko, 1998. "A placebo-controlled trial of the immune modulator, lentinan, in HIV – positive patients: a phase I/II trial" *Journal of Medicine* 29 (5-6): 305-330.

Grzywnowicz, K., 2001. "Medicinal mushrooms in Polish folk medicine" *International Journal of Medicinal Mushrooms* 3: 154.

Gunde-Cimerman, N.G. and A. Cimerman, 1995. "*Pleurotus* fruiting bodies contain the inhibitor of 3-hydroxy-3-methylglutaryl-Coenzyme A Reductase-Lovastatin®." *Experimental Mycology* 19: 1-6.

Gunde-Cimerman, N. 1999. "Medicinal value of the genus *Pleurotus* (Fr.) P. Kast. (Agaricales s.l., Basidiomycetes)" *International Journal of Medicinal Mushrooms*, vol. 1: pp. 69-80.

Haak-Frendscho, M., K. Kino, T. Sone et al. 1993. "Ling Zhi-8: a novel T cell mitogen induces cytokine production and up-regulation of ICAM-1 expression. *Cell Immunol*: 150(1): 101-13.

Halpern G.M., 1999. "Cordyceps: China's healing mushroom" Avery Publishing Group, Garden City Park, New York.

Han, M.D., H. Jeong, J.W. Lee, S. J. Back, S. U. Kim & K.H. Yoon, 1995. "The composition and bioactivities *of ganoderan by mycelial fraction of Ganoderma lucidum IY009.*" Korean Journal of Medicine 23: 285-297.

MycoMedicinals: *An Informational Treatise on Mushrooms*

Han, M.D., E.S. Lee, Y.K. Kim, 1998. "Production of nitric oxide in raw 264.7 macrophages treated with ganoderan, the beta glucan of *Ganoderma lucidum*. *Korean Journal of Mycology* 26:246-255.

Hang, KC., 1993. *The Pharmacology of Chinese Herbs*. Boca Raton, FL. CRC Press.

Hanssen, H.P., 1996. "The genus Ganoderma in Europe" in *Ganoderma lucidum*, A Medicinal Mushroom, *Ganoderma lucidum* Ganoderma, Polyporaceae and others. Oriental Tradition, Cultivation, Breeding, Chemistry, Biochemistry and Utilization of *Ganoderma lucidum*"ed. by T. Mizuno, pp. 179-192. Il-Yang Pharm Co.

Ganoderma lucidum, A Medicinal Mushroom, *Ganoderma lucidum* Ganoderma, Polyporaceae and others. Oriental tradition, Cultivation, Breeding, Chemistry, Biochemistry and Utilization of *Ganoderma lucidum*"ed. by T. Mizuno. Il-Yang Pharm Co.

Haranaka, K. N. Satomi, A. Sakurai, R. Haranaka, N. Okada, and M. Kobayishi, 1985. "Antitumor activities and tumor necrosis factor producibility of traditional Chinese medicines and crude drugs." *Cancer Immunology & Immunotherapy* 20(1): 1-5.

Hasegawa, K., R. Nishimura, M. Kinugasa, M. Okamura, A. Kimura, F. Ohstu, K. Tekeuchi, & V. Mizuhria, 1990. "Electron microscopic and immunological studies concerning the effect on the antitumor activity of sizofiran (SPG) combined with radiotherapy for cervical cancer" *Nippon-Gan-Chiryo-Gakkkai-Shi* Oct; 20: 25(10): 2549-61.

Hattori, M., 1997. "Inhibitory effects of components from *Ganoderma lucidum* on the growth of human immunodeficiency virus (HIV) and the Protease Activity" in *Proceedings of the 1st International Symposium on Ganoderma lucidum* in Japan, Nov. 17-18th, 128-135. Tokyo.

Hatvani, N. 2001. "Antibacterial effect of the culture fluid of L*entinus edodes* mycelium grown in submerged liquid culture." *International Journal of Antimicrobial Agents* Jan: 17(1):71-4.

Hawkins, E., 2001. "Arabinoxylane: immune support from mushrooms" *Natural Pharmacy* 21, 26.

Hayakawa, K., N. Mitsuhashi, Y. Saito, M. Takahashi, S. Katano, K. Shiojima, M. Furuta, & H. Niib, 1993. "Effect of Krestin (PSK) as adjuvant treatment on the prognosis after radical radiotherapy with non-small cell lung cancer" *AntiCancer Research* 13: 1815-1820.

Heinemann, P. 1993. *Agarici Austroamericani VIII. Agariceae* des régions intertropicales d'Amérique du Sud. *Bull. Jard. Bot. Belg.* 62: 355-384.

Hibino, Y., Y. Konishi, J.. Koike, T. Tabata, Y. Ohashi, and N. Sugano, 1994. "Productions of interferon-gamma and nitrite are induced in mouse splenic cells by a heteroglycan-protein fraction from culture medium of *Lentinus edodes* mycelia" *Immunopharmacology* July-Aug 28(1): 77-85.

Hilborn, M.I., 1942. "The biology of *Fomes fomentarius*" *Bulletin of the Maine Agricultural Experimental Station.* No. 409.

Hirasawa, M., N. Shouji, T. Neta, K. Fukushima & K. Takada, 1999. "Three kinds of antibacterial substances from *Lentinus edodes* (Berk.) Sing. (shiitake, an edible mushroom)" *International Journal of Antimicrobial Agents* Feb; 11(2):151-157

Hirotani M. & T. Furuya, 1986. "Ganoderic acid derivatives, highly oxygenated lanotane-type triterpenoids, from *Ganoderma lucidum.*" *Phytochemistry* 25: 1189-1193.

Hiyoshi, T., F. Mutsunori & F. Akasu, 1996. "*Cordyceps sinensis* effects on cardiopulmonary function of long-distance runners" *Japanese Journal of Physical Fitness and Sports Medicine* 45: 474.

Hobbs, C., 1995. *Medicinal Mushrooms: an Exploration of Tradition, Healing and Cultures.* Interweave Press.

Hodge, K.T., S.B. Krasnoff, and R.A. Humber. 1996."Tolypocladium inflatum is the anamorph of *Cordyceps subsessilis.*" *Mycologia* 88(5): 715-719.

Horio, H., M. Ohtsuru, 2001. "Maitake (*Grifola frondosa*) improve glucose tolerance of experimental diabetic rats" *Journal of Nutritional Science & Vitaminology* Feb;47(1):57-63.

Horner, W.E., E. Levetin & S.B. Lehrer, 1993. "Basidiospore allergen release: elution from intact spores" *Journal of Allergy and Clinical Immunology* 92(2):306-312.

Hsieh, T.C. & J.M. Wu, 2001. "Cell growth and gene modulatory activities of Yunzhi (Windsor Wunxi) from mushroom Trametes versicolor and in androgen-dependent and androgen-insensitive human prostate cancer cells." *International Journal of Oncology.* Jan., 18(1):81-88.

Hu, T., J. Chen, J. Xu, and Q. Yang, 1992. "Effects of polysaccharide-peptide of *Coriolus* and polysaccharide of *Ganoderma* on scavenging active oxygen species" *Acta. Biochemical et Biophysical Sinica* 5:465-470.

Hung, W.S., C.L. Fang, C.H. Su, W.F. Lai, Y.C. Chang & Y.H. Tsai, 2001. "Cytotoxicity and immunogenicity of SACCHACHITIN and its mechanism of action on skin wound healing." J. *Biomed. Mater. Res.* Jul;56(1):93-100.

Iino, Y., T. Yokoe, M. Maemura, J. Horiguchi, H. Takei, S. Ohwada, & Y. Morshita, 1995. "Immunochemotherapies versus chemotherapy as adjuvant treatment after curative resection of operable breast cancer." *AntiCancer Research* 15: 2907-2912.

Ikekawa, T., M.Nakanishi, N. Uehara, G. Chihara & F. Fukuoka, 1968. "Antitumor action of some basidiomycetes, especially *Phellinus linteus. Japanese Journal of Cancer Research* 59: 155-157.

Ikekawa, T., N. Uehara, Y. Maeda, M. Nakanishi and F. Fukuoka, 1969. "Antitumor activity of aqueous extracts of edible mushrooms." *Cancer Research* 29: 734-735.

Ikekawa, T., H. Maruyama, T. Miyano, A. Okura, Y. Sawaskai, K. Naito, K. Kawamura & K. Shiratori, 1985. "Proflamin, a new antitumor agent: preparation, physicochemical properties and antitumor activity. *Japanese Journal of Cancer Research* 76: 142-148.

Ikekawa, T., N. Uehara, Y. Maeda, M. Nakanishi, F. Fukuoka, 1989. "Twenty years of Studies on Antitumor Activities of Mushrooms". *Cancer Research* 29, 734-735.

Ikekawa, T., 2001. "Beneficial effects of edible and medicinal mushrooms on health care." *International Journal of Medicinal Mushrooms* 3: 291-298.

Inomata, T., Y. Ogawa, A. Nishioka, T. Maeda & H. Sequchi, 1990. "Improvement in the effects of radiation therapy with BRM" *Gan-No Rinsho* Oct; 36(1`3):2278-85.

Ito, H. & M. Sugiura & T. Miyazaki, 1976. "Antitumor polysaccharide fraction from the culture filtrate of *Fomes fomentarius" Chemical & Pharmacological Bulletin* Oct; 24(10): 2575.

Ito, H. and K. Shimura, 1986. "Studies on the antitumor activity of traditional Chinese medicines. (II). The antitumor mechanism of traditional Chinese medicines." *Gan To Kagaku Ryoho* 12(11):2149-54.

Ito, H., K. Shimura, H. Itoh, M. Kawade, 1997. "Antitumor effects of a new polysaccharide-protein complex (ATOM) prepared from A*garicus blazei* (Iwade strain 101) "Himematsutake" and its mechanisms in tumor-bearing mice" *Anticancer Research* Jan-Feb 17(1A): 277-84.

Itoh, H., H. Ito, H. Amano, and H. Noda, 1994. "Inhibitory action of a (1—>6)beta-D-glucan-protein complex (FIII-2-b) isolated from *Agaricus blazei* Murrill ("Himematsutake") on Meth A fibrosarcoma-bearing mice and its antitumor mechanism" *Japanese Journal of Pharmacology* Oct; (66) (2): 265-71.

Jong, S.C., J.M. Birmingham and S.H. Pai, 1991. "Immuno-modulatory substances of fungal origin."*Journal of Immunol. Immunopharamacol.* Vol. XI, N. 3.

Jong, S.C. & J.M Birmingham, 1992. "Medicinal benefits of the mushroom Ganoderma", 1992. *Advances in Applied Microbiology* vol. 37: 101-133.

Jong, S.C. and J.M. Birmingham, 1992. "Medicinal effects of the mushroom Ganoderma. "*Adv. Appl. Microbiol.* 37: 101-134.

Kabir, Y.M. & S. Kimura, 1987. Effect of shiitake (*Lentinus edodes*) and maitake (*Grifola frondosa*) mushrooms on blood pressure and plasma lipids of spontaneously hypertensive rats. *J. Nutr. Sci. Vitaminol.* 33: 341-346.

Kahlos, K., M.V. Schantz and R. Hiltunen, 1984. "3 ß-hydroxy-lanosta-8, 24-dien-21, a new triterpenes from *Inonotus obliquus. Acta Pharmaceutica Fennica* 92: 197-198.

Kahlos, K., 1986. "3 ß, 22-Dihydroxy-lanosta-8,24-dien-7-one, a new 7-keto compound from *Inonotus obliquus" Acta Pharmaceutica Fennica* 95, 113-117.

Kahlos K. & R. Hiltunen, 1986a. "Two oxygenated lanostane type triterpenes from *Inonotus obliquus" Acta Pharmaceutica Fennica* 95, 71-76.

Kahlos, K., L. Kangas & R. Hiltunen, 1986b. "Antitumour tests of inotodiol from the fungus" *Inonotus obliquus" Acta Pharmaceutica Fennica* 95: 173-177.

Kahlos, K., L. Kangas & R. Hiltunen, 1987a. "Antitumour activity of some compounds and fractions from an n-hexane extract of *Inonotus obliquus. Acta Pharmaceutica Fennica* 96: 33-40.

79

MycoMedicinals: *An Informational Treatise on Mushrooms*

Kahlos, K. & R. Hiltunen, 1987b. "Gas chromatographic mass spectrometric study of some sterols and lupines from *Inonotus obliquus*" *Acta Pharmaceutica Fennica* 96(2) 85-89.

Kahlos, K. & R. Hiltunen, 1988. "Gas chromatographic mass spectrometric identification of some lanostanes from *Inonotus obliquus*" *Acta Pharmaceutica Fennica* 97:45-49.

Kahlos, K. & R. Hiltunen & T. Vares, 1990. "Optimization of pH level and effect of pH on secondary metabolites of two strains of *Inonotus obliquus*" *Planta Medica* 56: 627.

Kahlos, K. et al., 1996. "Preliminary tests of antiviral activity of two *Inonotus obliquus* strains". *Fitopterapia* 6 (4) 344-7.

Kamm, YlJl, H.T. Folgering, H.G. van den Bogart, 1991. "Provocation tests in extrinsic allergic alveolitis in mushroom workers" *Netherlands Journal of Medicine* Feb. 38(1-2):59-64.

Kariya, K., K. Nakamura, K. Nomoto, S. Matama, and K. Saigneji, 1992. "Mimicking of superoxide dismutase activity by protein-bound polysaccharide of *Coriolus versicolor* QUEL., and oxidative stress relief for cancer patients" *Molecular Biotherapy* Mar; 4(1): 40-6.

Kawagishi, H., A. Nomura, T. Yumen, T. Mizuno, T. Hagwara and T. Nakamura, 1988. "Isolation and properties of a lectin from the fruiting bodies of *Agaricus blazei*" *Carbohydrate Research* Nov 15: 183(1): 150-4.

Kawagishi, H., R. Inagaki, T. Kanao, T. Mizuno, K. Shimura, H. Ito, T. Hagiwara, and T. Nakamura, 1989. "Fractionation and antitumor activity of the water insoluble residue of *Agaricus blazei* fruiting bodies" *Carbohydrate Research* Mar. 15; 186(2): 267-73.

Kawagishi, H., R. Katsumi, T. Sazawa, T. Mizuno, T. Hagiwara, and T. Nakamura, 1988. *Phytochemistry* 27, 2777.

Kawagishi et al., 1994. "Erinacines A, B, C, strong stimulators of nerve growth factor synthesis, from the mycelia of *Hericium erinaceum*." *Tetrahedron Letters* 35 (10): 1569-1572.

Kawagishi, H., A. Nomura, T. Mizuno, A. Kimura & S. Chiba, 1990. "Isolation and characterization of a lectin from *Grifola frondosa* fruiting bodies" *Biochimica-Biophysica-Acta* 1034: (3):247-252.

Kawagishi et al., 1991. "Hericenones C, D and E, Stimulators of nerve growth factor (NGF)-synthesis from the mushroom *Hericium erinaceum*." *Tetrahedron Letters*, vol. 32, no. 35, 4561-4564.

Kawakami, S., K. Minato, T. Hashimoto, H. Ashida & M. Mizuno, 2002. "TNF-alpha and NO production from macrophages is enhanced through up-regulation of NF-kB by polysaccharides purified from *Agaricus blazei* Murrill" *Proceedings of the 7th International Mycological Congress Oslo* 11-17 August, pg. 55.

Kawamura, Y., S. Uchiyma, Y. Saito, 1991. "Survey of radiocesium in domestic mushrooms on the market" *Eisei-Shikenjo-Hokoku* (109): 98-9.

Kenmoku, H., T. Shimai, T. Toyomasu, N. Kato & T. Sassa, 2002. "Erinacine Q, a new erinacines from *Hericium erinaceum*, and its biosynthetic route to erinacines C in the basidiomycete" *Bioscience Biotechnology & Biochemistry* Mar; 66(3)571-5.

Kidd, P. 2000. "The use of mushroom glucans and proteoglucans in cancer treatment" *Alternative Medicine Review* 5(1):4-27.

Kim, B.K., H.W. Kim and E.C. Choi, 1994. "Anti-HIV effects of *Ganoderma lucidum*." in *Ganoderma: Systematics, Phytopathology & Pharmacology: Proceedings of Contributed Symposium 59 A,B. 5th International Mycological Congress*. Vancouver.

Kim, H.M., S.B. Han, G.T. Oh, Y.H. Kim, D.H. Hong, N.D. Hong & I.D. Yoo, 1996. "Stimulation of humoral and cell mediated immunity by polysaccharide from mushroom *Phellinus linteus*" *International Journal of Immunopharmacology* May; 18(5): 295-303.

Kim, B.K., R.S. Kim, & H.W. Kim, 1997. "Effects of *Ganoderma lucidum* on human leukocytes" in *Proceedings of the 1st International Symposium on Ganoderma lucidum* in Japan, Nov. 17-18th, 87-89, Tokyo.

Kim, D.H., S.B. Shim, N.J. Kim & I.S. Jang, 1999. "Beta-glucuronidase-inhibitory activity and hepatoprotective effect of *Ganoderma lucidum*" *Biol. Pharm. Bull.* Feb; 22(2):162-4.

Kim, H.S., S. Kacew & B. M. Lee, 1999. "In vitro chemopreventive effects of plant polysaccharides (*Aloe barbadensis* Miller, *Lentinus edodes*, *Ganoderma lucidum* and *Coriolus versicolor*" Short communication. *Carcinogenesis* vol. 20 no. 8,1637-1640.

Kim K.C. & I.G. Kim, 1999. "*Ganoderma lucidum* extract protects DNA from strand breakage caused by hydroxyl radical and UV radiation" *International Journal of Molecular Medicine* Sep;4(3): 273-7.

Kim H.W. & B.K. Kim, 1999. "Biomedical triterpenoids of *Ganoderma lucidum* (Curt.:Fr.) P. Karst. (Aphyllophoromycetideae). *International Journal of Medicinal Mushrooms*, 1: 121-138.

Kim, K.C. & I.G. Kim, 1999. "*Ganoderma lucidum* extract protects DNA from strand breakage caused by hydroxyl radical and UV irradiation." *International Journal of Molecular Mycology* Sep; 4(3):273-7.

Kimura, Y., H. Tojima, S. Fukase & K. Takeda, 1994. "Clinical evaluation of sizofilan as assistant immunotherapy in the treatment of head and neck cancer." *Acta-Oto-Laryngologica Supplement* 511: 192-5.

Ko, J.L., C.I. Hsu, R.H. Lin, C.L. Kao, and J.Y. Lin, 1995. "A new fungal immunomodulatory protein, FIP-five isolated from the edible mushroom, *Flammulina velutipes* and its complete amino acid sequence." *European Journal of Biochemistry* Mar 1; 228(2):244-9.

Kobayashi, H., K. Matsunaga, & M. Fujii, 1993. "PSK as a chemopreventive agent" *Cancer Epidemiology, Biomarkers & Prevention* 2(3): 271-276.

Kobayashi, Y., K. Kariya, K. Saigenji, & K. Nakamura, 1994. "Suppression of cancer cell growth in vitro by the protein-bound polysaccharide of *Coriolus versicolor* QUEL (PS-K) with SOD mimicking activity" *Cancer Biotherapy* 9 (1): 63-69.

Kobayashi, Y., K. Kariya, K. Saigenji, & K. Nakamura, 1994. "Enhancement of anti-cancer activity of cisdiamineddicholoroplatinum by the protein-bound polysaccharide of *Coriolus versicolor* QUEL (PS-K) in vitro. *Cancer Biotherapy* Winter; 9(4)351-8.

Kobayashi, H., K. Matsunaga, & Y. Oguchi, 1995. "Antimetastatic effects of PSK (Krestin), a protein-bound polysaccharide obtained from basidiomycetes: an overview" *Cancer Epidemiology, Biomarkers & Prevention* 4(3);275-81.

Koc, Y., A.G. Urbano, E.B. Sweeney & R. McCaffrey, 1996. "Induction of apoptosis by cordycepin in ADA-inhibited TdT-positive leukemia cells" *Leukemia* Jun; 10(6):1019-24.

Kodama, N., K. Komuta & H. Nanba, 2002. "Can maitake MD fraction aid cancer patients?" *Alternative Medicine Review* Jun;7(3):236-9.

Kodama, E.N., R.P. McCaffrey, K. Yusa & H. Mitsuya, 2000. "Antileukemic activity and mechanism of action of cordycepin against terminal deoxynucleotidyl transferase-positive (TdT+) leukemic cells" *Bichem Pharmacol* 1:59(3): 273-81.

Koh JH, Yu KW, Suh HJ, Choi YM, Ahn TS., 2002. Activation of macrophages and the intestinal immune system by an orally administered decoction from cultured mycelia of *Cordyceps sinensis* *Biosci Biotechnol Biochem* Feb;66(2):407-11.

Kohda, H., W. Tokumoto, K Sakamoto et al., 1985. "The biologically active constituents of *Ganoderma lucidum*" *Chem. Pharm. Bull.* 33(4): 1367-74.

Konno, S., D.G. Tortorelis, S.A. Fullerton, A.A. Samadi, J. Hettiarcarchchi & H. Tazaki, 2001. "A possible hypoglycaemic effect of maitake mushroom on Type 2 diabetic patients" *Diabetes Medicine* Dec: 18(12):1010.

Kubo, K., H. Aoki, & H. Nanba, 1994. "Anti-diabetic activity present in the fruit body *Grifola frondosa* (Maitake)." *Biol. Pharm. Bull.* 17, 8: 1106-1110.

Kuo, Y.C., C.Y. Lin, W.J. Tsai, and C.L. Wu, C.F. Chen & M.S. Shiao, 1994. "Growth inhibitors against tumor cells in *Cordyceps sinensis* other than cordycepin and polysaccharides" *Cancer-Investigation* 12(6): 611-5.

Kuo, Y.C., W.J. Tsai, M.S. Shiao, C.F. Chen & C.Y. Lin, 1996. "*Cordyceps sinensis* as an immunomodulatory agent" *American Journal of Chinese Medicine*, vol. XXIV, No. 2, pp. 111-125.

Kuo, Y.C., W.J. Tsai, J.Y. Wang, S.C. Chang, C.Y. Lin & M.S. Shiao, 2001. "Regulation of bronchoalveolar lavage fluids cell function by the immunomodulatory agents for *Cordyceps sinensis*" *Life Science* Jan 19: 68(9):1067-82.

Kurashige, S., Y. Akuzawa, and F. Endo, 1997. "Effects of *Lentinus edodes*, *Grifola frondosa* and *Pleurotus ostreatus* administration on cancer outbreak, and activities of macrophages and lymphocytes in mice treated with a carcinogen, N-butyl-N-butanolnitrosoamine" *Journal of Immunopharmacology-and-Immunotoxicology* May; 19(2): 175-183.

MycoMedicinals: *An Informational Treatise on Mushrooms*

Lacaz, C. da S., E.M. Heins-Vaccari, N.T. De Melo & G.L. Hernandez-Arriagada, 1996. "Basidiomycosis: a review of the literature" *Revista do Instituto de Medicina Tropical de Sao Paulo* Sep-Oct; 38(5):379-390.

Leck, Charles. 1991. Mass extinction of European fungi. *Trends in Ecology and Evolution*. Vol. 6, No. 6, June.

Lee, J.H., S.M. Chuo, K.S. Song, N.D. Hong & I.D. Yoo, 1996. "Characterization of carbohydrate-peptide linkage of acidic heteroglycopeptide with immuno-stimulating activity from mycelium of *Phellinus linteus*" *Chemical and Pharmacological Bulletin* May' 44(5):1093-1095.

Lee, J.M., H. Kwon, H. Jeong, J.W. Lee, S.Y. Lee, S.J. Baek & Y.J. Surh, 2001. "Inhibition of lipid peroxidation and oxidative DNA damage by *Ganoderma lucidum*". *Phytotherapy Research* May: 15(3)245-9.

Lelley, J., 1997. *Die Heilkraft der Pilze: Gesund durch Mykotherapie* Der Econ Verlag ist ein Unternehmen, Dusseldorf und Munchen.

Leung, M.Y., K.P. Fung, and Y.M. Choy, 1997. "The isolation of an immunomodulatory and anti-tumor polysaccharide preparation from *Flammulina velutipes*." *Immunopharmacology* Jan; 35(3): 255-63.

Li, L.S., F. Zheng & Z.H. Liu, 1996. "Experimental study on effect of *Cordyceps sinensis* in ameriolating aminoglycoside induced nephrotoxicity" *Chung Kuo Chung His I Chieh Ho Tsa Chih.* Dec: 16(12): 733-7.

Li, Q., S. Wang, & C. Sun, 1992. "Clinical study of rapid bladder filling agent" *Chung-Kuo-Chung-Hsi-I-Chieh-Ho-Tsa-Chih* Sept. (12) 9: 533-4, 517.

Li, M., C., L.S. Lei, D.S. Liang et al., 2000. "Effect of *Ganoderma lucidum* polysaccharides on oxygen free radicals in murine peritoneal macrophages." *Zhongguo Yaolixue Yu Dulixue Zazhi Chi: Journal of Pharmacology Toxicology* 14: 65-68.

Li, S.P., P. Li, T.T. Dong, & K.W. Tsim, 2001. "Anti-oxidation activity of different types of natural *Cordyceps sinensis* and cultured Cordyceps mycelia" *Phytomedicine* May;8(3)207-12.

Li, S.P., Z.R. Su, T.T. Dong & K.W. Tsim, 2002. "The fruiting body and its caterpillar host of *Cordyceps sinensis* show close resemblance in main constituents and its anti-oxidation activity. *Phytomedicine* May;9(4):319-24.

Lieu, C.W., S.S. Lee, and S.Y. Wang, 1992. "The effect of *Ganoderma lucidum* on induction of differentiation in leukemic U937 cells." *Anticancer Research* Jul-Aug: 12(4): 1211-5.

Lin, J.M., C.C. Lin, M.F. Chen, T. Ujiie & A. Takada, 1995. "Radical scavenger and antihepatoxic activity of *Ganoderma formosanum*, *Ganoderma lucidum* and *Ganoderma neo-japonicum*" *Journal of Ethnopharmacology* Jun 23;47(1):33-41.

Lin, Z.-B, 1993. "Advances in the pharmacology of *Tremella* polysaccharides. From *Mushroom Biology and Mushroom Products*." S.T. Chang et al., 293-298. The Chinese University Press.

Lin, Y. & G. Wu, 1988. "Protective effect of *Polyporus umbellatus* polysaccharide on toxic hepatitis in mice." 9:345-348, from *Abstracts of Chinese Medicines* 1: 444.

Lin, Y., et al., 1987. "A double-blind treatment of 72 cases of chronic hepatitis with Lentinan injection." New Drugs and Clinical Remedies 6:362-363, from *Abstracts of Chinese Medicines* 2: 325.

Lin, Y., 1989. "Pharmacological and gastronomic effects of fungi and its applications." *Chemical Times*, no. 1, 12-21.

Lin, Y., C.C. Lin, H.F. Chiu, J.J. Yang & S.G. Lee, 1993. "Evaluation of the anti-inflammatory and liver-protective effects of *Anoectochilus formosanus*, *Ganoderma lucidum* and *Gynostermma pentaphyllum* in rats." *American. Journal of Chinese Medicine* 21: 59-69.

Lin, J.M., C.C. Lin, M.F.Chen, T. Ujiie & A. Takada, 1995. "Radical scavenging and antihepatoxic activity of *Ganoderma formosanum*, *Ganoderma lucidum* and *Ganoderma neo-japonicum*" *Journal of Ethnopharmacology* Jun. 23; 47(1):33-41.

Lin, I,H., D.M. Hau, & Y.H. Chang, 1996. "Restorative effect of *Coriolus versicolor* polysaccharides against gamma-irradiation induced spleen injury in mice." *Chung Kuo Yao Li Hsueh_Pao Acta Pharmacologica Sinica* Mar: 17(2): 102-104.

Liu, C., S. Lu, MR Li, 1992a. "Effects of *Cordyceps sinensis* (CS) on in vitro natural killer cells." *Chung Kuo Chung Hsi I Cheih Ho Tsa Chih* 12(5): 267-9, 259.

Liu, P., C. Liu & Y.Y. Hu, 1996. "Effect of fuzheng huayu recipe in treating post hepatitic cirrhosis" *Zhongguo Zhong Xi Yi Jie Ha Za Zhi* Aug;16(8):459-62.

Lowenstein, C.J. & S.H. Snyder, 1992. "Nitric oxide, a novel biological messenger" *Cell* 70: 705-707.

Lovy, A., B. Knowles, R. Labbe & L. Nolan, 1999. "Activity of edible mushrooms against the growth of human T4 leukemia cancer cells, and *Plasmodium falciparum*" *Journal of Herbs, Spices & Medicinal Plants* vol. 6(4): 49-57.

Maitake Products, Inc., Press Release of Feb. 1, 1998, Parasmus, New Jersey.

Manohar, V., N.A. Talpur, B.W. Echard, S. Liberman & H.G. Preuss, 2002. "Effects of a water-soluble extract of maitake mushroom on circulating glucose/insulin concentrations in KK mice" *Diabetes Obes Metab* Jan; 4(1):43-48.

Majstrik, V. and A. Lepsova, 1992. "Applicability of fungi to the monitoring of environmental pollution by heavy metals". In *Plants as Biomonitors*, Markert, B. (ed.), VCH, Weinheim, 365-378.

Manez, S., M.C. Recio, R. M. Giner & J.L. Rios, 1997. "Effect of selected triterpenoids on chronic dermal inflammation" *European Journal of Pharmacology* Sep 3;334(1): 103-105.

Maret, S., 1991. Fungi in Khanty folk medicine. *Journal of Ethnopharmacology* 31: 175-179.

Matsui, Y. Kawaguchi, M. Nakagawa, A Hon-Kwon, Y. Kamiyama, K. Kosuna, 1998. "Preventive Effect of Active Hexose Correlated Compound (AHCC) on the Recurrence of Postoperative Hepatocellular Carcinoma Patients" *XXXIIIrd Congress of the European Society for Surgical Research*, p74.

Matsushita, K., Y. Kuramitsu, Y. Ohiro, M. Obara, M. Kobayashi, Y.Q. Li M. & Hosokawa, 1998. "Combination therapy of active hexose correlated compound plus UFT significantly reduces the metastasis of rat mammary adenocarcinoma" *Anticancer Drugs* 9; 343-350.

Maruyama, H., K. Yamazaki, S. Murofushi, et al., 1989. "Antitumor activity of Sarcodon aspratus (Berk.) S. Ito and *Ganoderma lucidum* (Fr.) Karst. *J. Pharmacobiodyn* 1989; 12 (2): 118-23.

Min, B.S., J.J. Gao, N. Nakamura & M. Hattori, 2000. "Triterpenes from the spores of *Ganoderma lucidum* and their cytotoxicity against Meth-A and LLC tumor cells" *Chemical Pharmacology Bulletin* Jul;48(7):1026-33.

Ming, D., J. Chilton, F. Fogarty & G.H. Towers, 2002. "Chemical constituents of *Ganoderma applanatum* of British Columbia forests" *Fitopterapia* Apr;73(2):147-52.

Miyasaki, T., 1983. "Antitumor activity of fungal crude drugs." *Journal of Traditional Sino-Japanese Medicine* 4(1), 61-65.

Miyazaki, K., H. Mizutani, H. Katabuchi, K. Fukuma, S. Fujisaki & H. Okamura, 1995. "Activated (HLA-DR+) T-lymphocyte subsets in cervical carcinoma and effects of radiotherapy and immunotherapy with sizofiran on cell mediated immunity and survival" *Gynecologic Oncology* Mar;56(3):412-20.

Mizuno, M., M. Morimoto, K. Minato, & H. Tsuchida, 1998. "Polysaccharides from *Agaricus blazei* stimulate lymphocyte T-cell subsets in mice" *Bioscience Biotechnology & Biochemistry* Mar; 62(3):434-7.

Mizuno, T., 1988. "Development and utilization of bioactive substances from medicinal and edible mushroom fungi II. *Ganoderma lucidum*." *Chemical Times* 1989 (3) 50-60.

Mizuno, T, 1989. "Yamabushitake, *Hericium erinaceum*: Bioactive Substances and Medicinal Utilization" *Food Reviews International* 11(1), 173-178.

Mizuno, T, 1989. "Pharmacological and gastronomic effects of fungi and its applications." *Chemical Times* 1: 12-21.

Mizuno, T, ed., 1995. "Mushrooms: The versatile fungus- food and medicinal properties" in *Food Reviews International*, vol. 11, no.1. Marcel Dekker, Inc., New York.

Mizuno, T. & B.K. Kim, 1996. . *A medicinal mushroom, Ganoderma lucidum* Il-Yang Pharm. Co., Seoul, Korea

Mizuno, T, H. Ito, K. Shimura, T. Hagiwara & T. Nakamura, 1989. "Preparation method of antitumor neutral polysaccharides from Himematsutake" *Japan Kokai Tokkyo Koho* (A), Sho64-67195, March 13, 565-568.

MycoMedicinals: *An Informational Treatise on Mushrooms*

Mizuno, T, H. Ito, K. Shimura, T. Hagiwara & T. Nakamura, 1989. "Preparation method of antitumor acidic glycans from Himematsutake" *Japan Kokai Tokkyo Koho* (A), Sho64-67194, March 13, 561-564.

Mizuno, T, Hagiwara, T., Nakamura, T., Ito, H. Shimura, K. Sumiya, T., Asakura, A. 1990. "Antitumor activity and some properties of water-soluble polysaccharides from 'Himematsutake,' the fruiting body of *Agaricus blazei* Murrill" *Agricultural & Biological Chemistry* 54. Tokyo. 2889-2896.

Mizuno, T, Hagiwara, T., Nakamura, T., Ito, H. Shimura, K. Sumiya, T., Asakura, A. 1990. "Antitumor activity and some properties of water-insoluble hetero-glycans from 'Himematsutake,' the fruiting body of *Agaricus blazei* Murrill" *Agricultural & Biological Chemistry* 54. Tokyo. 2897-2905.

Mizuno, T, T. Waa, H. Ito, C. Suzuki, N. Ukai, 1992. "Antitumor-active polysaccharides isolated from the fruitbody of *Hericium erinaceum*, an edible and medicinal mushroom called yamabushitake or houtou" *Biosci. Biotech. Biochem.* Feb; 56(2): 347-8.

Mizuno, T, H. Saito, T. Nishitoba, & H. Kawagishi, 1995a. "Antitumor active substances from mushrooms." *Food Reviews International* 111: 23-61. Marcel Dekker, New York.

Mizuno, T & C. Zhuang, 1995b. "Maitake, *Grifola frondosa*, pharmacological effects" *Food Reviews International* 111: 135-149. Marcel Dekker, New York.

Mizuno, T. C. Zhuang, K. Abe, H. Okamoto, T. Kiho, S. Ukai, S. Leclerc & L. Meijer, 1996. "Studies on the host-mediated antitumor polysaccharides, Part XXVII. Mushroom Science & Biotechnology 3(2), 53-60.

Mizuno, T., C. Zhuang, K. Abe, H. Okamoto, T. Kiho, S.Ukai S. Leclerc & L. Meijer, 1999. "Antitumor and hypoglycemic activities of polysaccharides from the sclerotia and mycelia of *Inonotus obliquus* (Pers.:Fr.) Pil. (Aphyllophoromycetideae). *International Journal of Medicinal Mushrooms* I; 301-316.

Mondoa, E. & Mindy Kitei, 2001. *Sugars that heal: the new healing science of glyconutrients* Ballantine Publishing Group, New York.

Mori, H.1987. "Effect of immunostimulants and antitumor agents on tumor necrosis factor (TNF) production." *Int. J. Immunopharmacol.* 9: 881-885.

Morigawa, A., K. Kitabatake, Y. Fujimoto, & N. Ikekawa, 1986. "Angiotensin converting enzyme-inhibiting triterpenes from *Ganoderma lucidum*" *Chemical and Pharmaceutical Bulletin* 34(7): 3025-3028.

Morinaga, H., K. Tazawa, H. Tagoh, A. Muraguchi, and M. Fujimaka, 1994. "An *in vivo* study of hepatic and splenic interleukin-1 beta mRNA expression following oral PSK or LEM administration" *Japanese Journal of Cancer Research* Dec. 85(12): 1298-1303.

Muramatsu, Y., S. Yoshida, and M. Sumiya, 1991. "Concentrations of radiocesium and potassium in basidiomycetes collected in Japan" *Science of the Total Environment* June 105: 29-39.

Murasugi, A., S. Tanaka, N. Komiyama, N. Iwata, K. Kino, H. Tsunoo, and S. Sakuma, 1991. "Molecular cloning of a cDNA and a gene encoding an immunomodulatory protein, Ling Zhi-8, from a fungus, *Ganoderma lucidum*" *Journal of Biological Chemistry* Feb 5; 266(4): 2486-93.

Murrill, W.A., 1945. "New Florida Fungi" *Journal of Florida Academy of Sciences*, vol. 8, no. 2, pp. 175-198.

Naeshiro, H. 1992. "Skin lightening compositions containing Ganoderma extract" *Japan Kokai Tokkyo Koho* JP 04 09, 315 (92 09, 315).

Nagao, T., M. Komatsuda, K. Yamauchi, H. Nozaki, K. Watanabe, S. Arimori, 1981. "Chemoimmunotherapy with Krestin in Acute Leukemia" *Tokai Journal of Experimental Clinical Medicine*, vol. 6, no. 2, pp. 141-146.

Nakahara, W., R. Tokuzen, F. Fukuoka, & R.L. Whistle. *Nature* 216: 374-375.

Nakajima, T., S. Ichikawa, S. Uchida, & T. Komada, 1990. "Effects of a protein bound polysaccharide from a basidiomycetes against hepatocarcinogenesis induced by 3'-methyl-4-dimethylaminoazobenzene in rats" *Clinical Therapeutics* 12(5):385-392.

Nakazato, H., A .Koike, S. Saji, N. Ogawa, J. Sakamoto, 1994. "Efficacy of immunotherapy as adjuvant treatment after curative resection of gastric cancer" *The Lancet* vol. 343, May 7, pp. 1122-1126.

84

References

Nanba, H. 1987. "The chemical structure of an antitumor polysaccharide in fruitbodies of *Grifola frondosa* (Maitake)." *Chemical and Pharmaceutical Bulletin* 35: 1162-8

Nanba, H., 1992. "Immunostimulant activity in-vivo and anti-HIV activity in-vitro of 3 branched ß-1-6 glucans extracted from Maitake mushroom (*Grifola frondosa*)." From the published abstracts of the *Proceedings of the VIII International Conference on AIDS and the III STD World Congress.*

Nanba, H., 1993. "Antitumor activity of orally administered D-fraction from Maitake Mushroom." *J. Naturopathic Med.* 41: 10-15.

Nanba, H., 1995. "Activity of Maitake D-Fraction to Inhibit Carcinogenesis and Metastasis." *Annals of the New York Academy of Sciences*, vol. 768: 243-245.

Nanba, H., 1997. "Maitake D-fraction: Healing and Preventative Potential for Cancer." *Journal of Orthomolecular Medicine* vol. 12: 43-49.

Naoki et al., 1994. "Pharmacological studies on *Cordyceps sinensis* from China." *Abstracts from the Fifth Mycological Congress.* Vancouver, BC, August 14-21.

Ng, T.B., J.M. Ling, Z.T. Wang, J.N. Cai, and G.J. Xu, 1996. "Examination of courmarins, flavonoids and polysaccharopeptide for antibacterial activity" *General Pharmacology* Oct; 27(7): 1237-40.

Ng, T.B., 1998. "A review of research on the protein-bound polysaccharide (polysaccharopeptide, PSP) from the mushroom *Coriolus versicolor*" *General Pharmacology* Jan; 30(1): 1-4.

Nishitoba, T., H. Saot, S. Shirasu, & S. Sakamura, 1987. "Novel triterpenoids from the mycelial mat at the previous stage of fruiting of *Ganoderma lucidum*." *Agricultural & Biological Chemistry* 51(2): 619-622.

Odani, S., K. Tominaga, S. Kondou, H. Hori, T. Koide, S. Hara, M. Isemura, & S. Tsunasawa, 1999. "The inhibitory properties and primary structure of a novel serine proteinase inhibitor from the fruiting body of the basidiomycete, *Lentinus edodes*." *European Journal of Biochemistry,* June 262(3): 915-923.

Oguchi, Y. 1987. "Effect of PSK on cytotoxicity against sarcoma 180 in tumor-bearing mice." *Anticancer Research.* Pt. B 7: 681-4.

Oh, J.Y., K. J. Cho, S. H. Chung et al., 1998. "Activation of macrophages by GLB, a protein-polysaccharide of the growing tips of *Ganoderma lucidum*. *Yakhak Hoeji* 42, 302-306.

Oh-hara, T., Y. Ikeda, H. Sakagami, K. Konno, T. Kaiya, K. Kohda, and Y. Kawazoe, 1990. "Lignified natural products as potential medicinal resources: Potentiation of hemolytic plaque-forming cell production in mice" *Chem. Pharm. Bull.* 38(1) 282-284.

Ohsawa, T., M. Yukawa, C. Takao, M. Murayama & H. Bando, 1992. "Studies on the constituents of fruitbody of *Polyporus umbellatus* and their cytotoxic activity" *Chem Pharm Bull.* Jan 40:143-147.

Ooi, V.E. & F. Liu, 1999. "A review of pharmacological activities of mushroom polysaccharides". *International Journal of Medicinal Mushrooms*, I: 195-206.

Ooi, V.E. & F. Liu, 2000. "Immunomodulation and anti-cancer activity of polysaccharide-protein complexes" *Curr Med Chem* July; 7(7):710-729.

Ooi, L.S., V.E.Ooi & M.C. Fung, 2002. "Induction of gene expression of the immunomodulatory cytokines in the mouse by a polysaccharide from *Ganoderma lucidum* (Curt.; Fr.) P. Karst. (Aphyllophoromycetideae)*" International Journal of Medicinal Mushrooms* 4: 27-35.

Ohno, N., I. Suzuki, S. Okawa, K. Sato, T. Miyazaki, and T. Yadomae, 1984. "Antitumor activity and structural characterization of glucans extracted from cultured fruitbodies of *Grifola frondosa*." *Chemical and Pharmaceutical Bulletin* Mar; 32(3): 1142-51.

Ohno, N., K. Iino, T. Takeyama, I. Suzuki, K. Sato, S. Oikawa, T. Miyazaki, & T. Yadomae, 1985. "Structural characterization and antitumor activity of the extracts from matted mycelium of cultured *Grifola frondosa*." *Chemical and Pharmaceutical Bulletin* 33 (8)3395-3401.

Ohno, N., N. Asada, Y. Adachi, and T. Yadomae, 1995. "Enhancement of LPS triggered TNF-alpha (tumor necrosis factor-alpha) production by 1—>3)-beta-D-glucans in mice." *Biol. Pharm. Bull.*, Jan; 18(1)126-33.

Ohsawa, T., M. Yukawa, C. Takao, M. Murayama, H. Bando, 1992. "Studies on the constituents of the fruit body *Polyporus umbellatus* and their cytotoxic activity" *Chemical and Pharmaceutical Bulletin* Tokyo. Jan 40(1): 143-147.

MycoMedicinals: *An Informational Treatise on Mushrooms*

Ohtomo, M., 2001. "*In vivo* and *in vitro* test study: physiological activity in immune response system of representative basidiomycetes." Unpublished data. Personal communication re: testing of Fungi Perfecti® products. Tamagawa University, Japan.

Oka et al., 1992. "Immunological analysis and clinical effects of intraabdominal and intrapleural injection of lentinan for malignant ascites and pleural effusion." *Biotherapy* 5: 107-112.

Okamoto, K., et al. 1993. "Antimicrobial chlorinated orcinol derivatives from mycelium of *Hericium erinaceus.*" *Phytochemistry*, vol. 34, no. 5, 1445-1446.

Okazaki, M., Y. Adachi, N. Ohno, T. Yadomae, 1995. "Structure-activity relationship of (1—3)-beta-D-glucans in the induction of cytokine production from macrophages, *in vitro.*" *Biological and Pharmaceutical Bulletin* Oct. 18(10): 1320-7.

Ooi, V. and F. Liu (1999) "A review of the pharmacological activities of mushroom polysaccharides" in the *International Journal of Medicinal Mushrooms*, vol. 1, pp. 195-196.

Osaki, Y., T. Kato, K. Yamamto, J. Okubo, T. Miyazaki, 1994. "Antimutagenic and bactericidal substances in the fruit body of a Basidiomycete *Agaricus blazei*" *Journal of the Pharmaceutical Society of Japan* May; 114(5): 342-50.

Pegler, D.N., Y.J. Yao, & Y. Li, 1994. "The Chinese Caterpillar Fungus" *The Mycologist* 8: 3-5.

Peintner, U., R. Poder, & T. Pumpel, 1998. The Ice Man's fungi. *Mycological Research* 102 (10): 1153-1162.

Pereira, J. 1843. "Summer Plant, Winter Worm" *New York Journal of Medicine* I: 128-132.

Piraino, F. & C. Brandt, 1999. "Isolation and partial characterization of an antiviral, RC-183, from the edible mushroom, *Rozites caperata*" *Antiviral Research* 43: 67-68.

Pisha, E., H. Chai, I.S. Lee, T.E. Chagwedera, N.R. Farnsworth, G.A Cordell, C.W. Beecher, H.H. Fong, A.D. Kinghorn & D.M Brown, 1995 "Discovery of betulinic acid as a selective inhibitor of human melanoma that functions by induction of apoptosis" *Nature Medicine* Oct;1(10):1046-51.

Protiva, J., H. Skorkovska, J. Urban & A. Vystrcil, 1980. "Triterpenes and steroids from *Ganoderma applanatum*" *Collect. Czech. Chem. Comm.* 45 10:2710-2713.

Reshetnikov, S., S.P. Wasser and K.K. Tan, 2001. "Higher Basidiomycota as a source of antitumor and immunostimulating polysaccharides (review)" *International Journal of Medicinal Mushrooms*, vol. 3, pp. 361-394.

Rhis, J.D., A.A. Padhye & C.B. Good, 1996. "Brain abscess caused by Schizophyllum commune: an emerging basidiomycete pathogen" *Journal of Clinical Microbiology* Jul; 34(7):1628-32.

Rosecke, J & W.A. Konig, 2000. "Constituents of various wood-rotting Basidiomycetes" *Phytochemistry* Jul;54(6):603-10.

Saar, M., 1991. "Fungi in Khanty folk medicine" *Journal of Ethnopharmacology* Feb; 31(2):175-179.

Sakagami, Y, Y. Mizoguchi, T. Shin, S. Seki, K. Kobayashi, S. Morisawa & S. Yamaoto, 1988. "Effects of anti-tumor polysaccharide, schizophyllan, on interferon-gamma and interleukin 2". *Biochemistry & Biophysical Research Communication* Sept 15; 155(2): 650-5.

Sakagami, H., T. Aoki, A. Simpson, & S.I. Tanuma, 1991. "Induction of immunopotentiation activity by a protein-bound polysaccharide, PSK" *Anticancer Research* 11:993-1000.

Sakagami, H., K. Sugaya, A. Utsumi, S. Fujinaga, T. Sato and M. Takeda, 1993. "Stimulation by PSK of interleukin-1 production by human peripheral blood mononuclear cells" *Anticancer Research*, May-June 13(3): 671-5.

Samania, A., F. Delle Monache, E.F.A. Smania and R.S. Cuneo, 1999. "Antimicrobial activity of steroidal compounds isolated from *Ganoderma applanatum* (Pers.) Pat. (Aphyllophoromycetideae) fruitbody" *International Journal of Medicinal Mushrooms*, vol. 1, pp. 325-330.

Sanzen, I., N. Imanishi, N. Takamatsu, S. Konosu, N. Mantani, K. Terasaw, K. Tazaw, Y. Odaira, M. Watanabe, M. Takeyama & H. Ochiai, 2001. "Nitric oxide-mediated antitumor activity induced by the extract of *Grifola frondosa* (Maitake mushroom) in a macrophage cell line, RAW264.7" *Journal of Experimental Clinical Cancer Research* Dec; 20(4):591-7.

Sarkar, S., J. Koga, R.J. Whitley, and S. Chatterjee, 1993. Antiviral effect of the extract of culture medium of *Lentinus edodes* mycelia on the replication of herpes simplex virus 1. *Antiviral Research.* April 20(4): 293-303.

Sasaki, T., Y. Arai, T. Ikekawa, G. Chihara & F. Fukuoka, 1971. "Antitumor polysaccharides from some Polyporaceae, *Ganoderma applanatum* (Pers.) Pat and *Phellinus linteus* (Berk. et Curt.) Aoshima" *Chemical and Pharmacological Bulletin* Apr; 19(4):821-826.

Schlegel, B., U. Luhmann, A. Hartl & U. Grafe, 2000. "Piptamine, a new antibiotic produced by *Piptoporus betulinus* Lu 9-1." *Journal of Antibiotics* Sep; 53(9):973-4.

Shigesue, K., N. Kodama & H. Nanba, 2000. "Effects of maitake (*Grifola frondosa*) polysaccharide on collagen-induced arthritis in mice" *Japanese of Journal Pharmacology* Nov; 84(3): 293-300.

Shi, Y.L., I.F.F. Benzie, & J.A. Buswell, 2002. "Genoprotective activities of mushrooms" *Proceedings of the 7th International Mycological Congress Oslo* 11-17 August, pg. 54.

Shin, Y., Y. Tamai, M. Terazawa, 2000a. "Chemical constituents of *Inonotus obliquus* I." *Eurasian Journal of Forestry Research* 1:43-50.

Shin, Y., Y. Tamai & M. Terazawa, 2000b. "Chemical constituents of *Inonotus obliquus* (Pers.:Fr.) Pil. (Aphyllophoromycetideae) III: a new triterpene, 3ß, 22,25-trihydrozy-lanosta-8-ene from sclerotia" *International Journal of Medicinal Mushrooms*, vol. 2: 201-207.

Shin, Y., Y. Tamai, M. Terazawa, 2001c. "Chemical constituents of *Inonotus obliquus* IV." *Eurasian Journal of Forestry Research* 2:27-30.

Shon, Y.H. & K.S. Nam, 2001. "Antimutagenicty and induction of anticarcinogenic phase II enzymes by basidiomycetes" *Journal of Ethnopharmacology* Sep; 77(1):103-9.

Sia, G.M. & J.K. Candlish, 1999. "Effect of shiitake (*Lentinus edodes*) extract on human neutrophils and the U937 monocytic cell line" *Phytotherapy Research* Mar; 13(2): 133-137.

Small, E.J., M.W. Frohlich, & R. Bok, 2000. "Prospective trial of the herbal supplement PC-SPES in patients with progressive prostate cancer" *Journal of Clinical Oncology* 18: 3595-3603.

Song, K.S., S.M. Cho, J. H. Lee, H.M. Kim, S.B. Han, K.S. Ko & I.D. Yoo, 1995. "B-lymphocyte-stimulating polysaccharide from mushroom *Phellinus linteus*" *Chemical and Pharmacological Bulletin* Dec; 43(12):2105-2108.

Soo, T.S., 1994. "The therapeutic value of *Ganoderma lucidum*." *Proceedings of Contributed Symposium 59* A,B. *5th International Mycological Congress*. Vancouver. 105-113.

Stamets, P., 2000 "Techniques for the Cultivation of the Royal Sun Agaricus, *Agaricus blazei* Murrill Himematsutake on Compost and Wood Substrates" *International Journal of Medicinal Mushrooms*, vol. 2, pp. 151-160.

Stamets, P., 2001a. "New Anti-viral compounds from mushrooms". *Herbalgram* 51:24,27.

_____, 2001b. "The ancient polypore: Bridgeoporus nobilissimus, a mushroom of many mysteries" *Herbalgram* 51: pg. 25-26.

_____, 2002. "Novel antimicrobials from mushrooms" *Herbalgram* 54: 29-33.

Stavinoha, W.B., S. Weintraub, T. Opham, A. Colorado, R. Opieda, J. Slama, 1990. Study of the anti-inflammatory activity of *Ganoderma lucidum*." *Proceedings from the Academic/Industry Conference* (AIJC), August 18-20, Sapporo, Japan.

Stavinoha, W.B., J.T. Slama & S. T. Weintraub, 1996. "The anti-inflammatory activity of *Ganoderma lucidum* 6.1" pp.193-196. in *Ganoderma lucidum*, A Medicinal Mushroom, *Ganoderma lucidum* Ganoderma, Polyporaceae and others. Oriental Tradition, Cultivation, Breeding, Chemistry, Biochemistry and Utilization of *Ganoderma lucidum*" ed. by T. Mizuno. Il-Yang Pharm Co.

Stavinoha, W.B., 1997. "Status of *Ganoderma lucidum* in United States: *Ganoderma lucidum* as an anti-inflammatory agent" Proceedings of the 1st International Symposium on *Ganoderma lucidum* in Japan. Nov. 17-18th, 99-103. Tokyo.

Steinkraus, D.C. & J.B. Whitfield, 1994. "Chinese Caterpillar Fungus and World Records" *American Entomologist* Winter 235-239.

Stijve, T., 1977. "Selenium content of mushrooms". *Z. Lebensmittel-Untersuchung und-Forschung* 164: 201-203.

Stijve, T., 1984. "Inorganic bromide in higher fungi". *Z. Naturforsch.* 39c, 863-866.

Stijve, T., C. E. Vellinga, & A. Herrman, 1990. "Arsenic accumulation in some higher fungi" *Persoonia* 14: 2, 161-166.

MycoMedicinals: *An Informational Treatise on Mushrooms*

Stijve, T., & B. Bourqui, 1991. "Arsenic in edible mushrooms". *Deutsche Lebensmittel-Rundschau* 87. Jahrg. Heft 10: 307-310.

Stijve, T., 1992. "Certain mushrooms do accumulate heavy metals." *Mushroom, the Journal of Wild Mushrooming*: 38: II, No. 1., 9-14.

Stijve, T. & M.A.L. de A. Amazonas. 2001. "*Agaricus blazei* Murrill, un nouveau champignon gourmet et medicament qui nous vient du Brésil" *Miscellanea Mycologica* 69: 41-47.

Stijve, T., 2001. Personal communication.

Sugano et al., 1982. "Anti carcinogenic actions of water-soluble and alcohol-insoluble fractions from culture medium of *Lentinus edodes* mycelia." *Cancer Letters* 17: 109-114.

Suay, I, F. Arenal, F. Asenio, A. Basilio, M. Cabello, M.T. Diez, J. B. Garcia, A. Gonzalez del Val, J. Gorrochategui, P. Hernandez, F. Pelaez, M. F. Vicente, 2000. "Screening of basidiomycetes for antimicrobial activities" *Antonie van Leeuwenhoek* 78: 129-139.

Sudirman, L., 1999. "Preliminary detection of antimicrobial activity of fruiting body extracts tropical Ganoderma sp." AMATO. http://www.kyotan.com/lectures/lectures/Lecture 12.html.

Sugimachi, K., Y. Maehara, M. Ogawa, T. Kakegawa and M. Tomita, 1997. "Dose intensity of uracil and tegafur in postoperative chemotherapy for patients with poorly differentiated gastric cancer" *Cancer Chemotherapy and Pharmacology* 40(3): 233-8.

Sugiyama, K., T. Akachi & A. Yamakawa, 1995. "Hypocholesterolemic action of eritadenine is mediated by a modification of hepatic phospholipid metabolism in rats" *Journal of Nutrition*, Aug; 125(8):2134-44.

Suzuki, I., T. Itani, N. Ohno, S. Oikawa, K. Sato, T. Miyazaki, T. Yadomae, 1984. "Antitumor activity of a polysaccharide fraction extracted from cultured fruitbodies of *Grifola frondosa*." *Journal of Pharmacobiodyn.* Jul; 7(7): 492-500.

Suzuki, I.,, K. Hashimoto, S. Oikawa, K. Sato, M. Osawa, T. Yadomae, 1989. "Antitumor and immunomodulating activities of a beta-glucan obtained from liquid-cultured *Grifola frondosa*." *Chemical and Pharmaceutical Bulletin* Feb; 37(2): 410-3.

Suzuki, H., A. Okubo, S. Yamazaki, K. Suzuki, H. Mitsuya & S. Toda, 1989. "Inhibition of the infectivity and cytopathic effect of human immunodeficiency virus by water soluble lignin in an extract of the culture medium of *Lentinus edodes* mycelia (LEM)" *Biochemical and Biophysical Research Communications* vol. 160, no. 1.

Suzuki, H., K. Iiyama, O. Yoshida, S. Yamazaki, N. Yamamoto, and S. Toda, 1990. "Structural characterization of immunoactive and antiviral water-solubilized lignin in an extract of the culture medium of *Lentinus edodes* mycelia (LEM)" *Agricultural and Biological Chemistry* Feb. 54(2): 479-87.

Taguchi et al., 1982. "Clinical trials on lentinan (polysaccharide)." In Yamamura, Y. et al. (eds) Immunomodulation by Microbial Products and Related Synthetic Compounds, pp. 467-475. *Elsevier Science Pub. Co.*, New York.

Takeyama, T., I. Suzuki, N. Ohno, S. Oikawa, K. Sato, M. Ohsawa, T. Yadomae, 1987. "Host-mediated antitumor effect of Grifolan NMF-5N, a polysaccharide obtained from *Grifola frondosa*" *Journal of Pharmacobio-dynamics* Nov. 10(11): 644-51.

Takaku, T., Y. Kimura & H. Okuda, 2001. "Isolation of an antitumor compound from *Agaricus blazei* Murill (sic) and its mechanism of action" *Journal of Nutrition* May 131(5):1409-1413.

Tao, J. and K.Y.Feng, 1990. "Experimental and clinical studies on inhibitory effect of *Ganoderma lucidum* on platelet aggregation" *Journal of Tongji Medical University* 10(4): 240-3.

Tochikura et al., 1987. "A biological response modifier, PSK, inhibits immunodeficiency virus infection in vitro." *Biochem. Biophys. Res. Commun.* 148: 726-733.

Tokuyama, T., Y. Hayashi, M. Nishizawa, H. Toruda, S.M Chairul & Y. Hayashi, 1991. "Applanoxidic acids A, B, C & D, Biologically active tetracyclic triterpenes from *Ganoderma applanatum*" *Phytochemistry* 30 12:4105-4109.

Tomoda, M., R. Gonda, Y. Kasahara, and H. Hikino, 1986. "Antidiabetes drugs. Glycan structures of ganoderans B and D, hypoglycemic glycans of *Ganoderma lucidum* fruit bodies." *Phytochemistry* 25: 2817-2820.

Torisu, M., Y. Hayashi, T. Ishimitsu, T. Fujimora, K. Iwasaki, M. Katano, H. Yamamoto, Y. Kimura, M. Takesue, M. Kondo & K. Nomoto, 1990. "Significant prolongation of disease-free period gained by oral polysaccharide K (PSK) administration after curative surgical operation of colorectal cancer". *Cancer Immunology Immunotherapy* 31:261-268.

Trutneva, I.A. & L. F. Gorovoj, 2001. "The mechanisms of mushroom glucan activity in the Mycoton Preparation" *International Journal of Medicinal Mushrooms*, vol. 3, pp. 234-235.

Turner, N.J., R. Bouchard & D.I.D. Kennedy, 1980. "Ethnobotany of the Okanagan-Colville Indians of British Columbia and Washington" *Occasional Papers of the British Columbia Provincial Museum. Province of British Columbia*, 21: 16-17.

Tsujinaka, T., M. Yokota, J. Kambayashi, M.C. Ou, Y. Kido, and T. Mori, 1990. "Modification of septic processes by beta-glucan administration" *European Surgical Research* 22(6): 340-346.

Tsukagoshi, S., Y. Hashimoto, G. Fujii, H. Kobayashi, K. Nomoto, K. Orita, 1984. "Krestin (PSK)." *Cancer Treatment Review* 11:131-155.

Tsunoo, A., N. N. Takemoto, H. Tsuboi, M. Kamiho, A. Nemoto, H. Sasaki, M. Uchida, 1995. "Cordyceps sinensis: its diverse effects on mammals *in vitro* and *in vivo*." *New Initiatives in Mycological Research: Proceedings of the Third International Symposium of the Mycological Society of Japan.*

Ukai, S., T. Kiho, C. Hira, I. Kuruma & Y. Tanaka, 1983. "Polysaccharides in fungi. XIV. Anti-inflammatory effect of the polysaccharides from the fruitbodies of several fungi." *Journal of Pharmacobiodynamics* Dec; 6(12):983-90.

Usui, S., Y. Tomono, M. Sakai, T. Kiho & S. Ukai, 1995. "Preparation of antitumor activities of beta-(1‡6) branched (1—3)-beta-D-glucan derivatives" *Biological & Pharmaceutical Bulletin* Dec; 18(12): 1630-6.

Vole, J., N.P. Denisova, F. Nerud & V. Musilek, 1985. "Glucose-2-oxidase activity in mycelial cultures of basidiomycetes" *Folia Microbiologica* (Praha) 30(2): 141-147.

Wang J. et al., 1985. "Study of the action of *Ganoderma lucidum* on scavenging hydroxyl radical from plasma." *Journal of Traditional Chinese Medicine* 5: 44-60.

Wang, S.Y., M.L. Hsu, H.C. Hsu, C.H. Tzeng, S.S. Le, M.S. Shiao, & C.K. Ho, 1997. "The anti-tumor effect of *Ganoderma lucidum* is mediated by cytokines released from activated macrophages and T lymphocytes." *International Journal of Cancer*. 70(6): 669-705.

Wang, H.X. and T.B. Ng, 2000. "Isolation of a novel ubiquitin-like protein from *Pleurotus ostreatus* mushroom with anti-human immunodeficiency virus, Translation-inhibitory and ribonuclease activities" *Biochemical and Biophysical Research Communications* 276: 587-593.

Wang, S.Y. & M.S. Shiao, 2000. "Pharmacological functions of Chinese medicinal fungus *Cordyceps sinensis* and related species" *Journal of Food and Drug Analysis* vol. 8; no. 4, 248-257.

Wasser, S.P., 1999. *International Journal of Medicinal Mushrooms* vol. 1, no. 1, ed. Begell House, New York.

Wasser, S.P. & Weis, A.L., 1999. Medicinal properties of substances occurring in higher basidiomycetes mushrooms: current perspectives (Review) *International Journal of Medicinal Mushrooms*, vol. 1, 31-62.

Wasser, S.P., 2002. Personal communication.

Wedam, N. & Haynes, A., 1997. "Breast cancer" *Journal of Naturopathic Medicine*, vol. 7, no. 2,. 86-87.

Weil, A., 1997. Personal communication.

Wu, TN., KC Yang, CM Wang, et al., 1996. "Lead poisoning caused by contaminated Cordyceps, a Chinese herbal medicine" *Science of the Total Environment* 182(1-3), 193-195.

Xiong, L., 1993. "Therapeutic effect of combined therapy of Salvia miltiorrhizae and *Polyporus umbellatus* polysaccharide in the treatment of chronic hepatitis B." *Chung-Kuo-Chung-Hsi-I-Chieh-Ho-Tsa-Chih* Sept. 13(9): 533-5; 516-7.

Xu, CP., 1985. "A double-blind study of effectiveness of *Hericium erinaceus* per therapy on chronic atrophic gastritis. A preliminary report." *Chinese Medical Journal* 98(6): 455-456.

MycoMedicinals: *An Informational Treatise on Mushrooms*

Xu, HM., 1994. "Immunomodulatory function of polysaccharide of *Hericium erinaceus*" *Chung Kuo Chung Hsi I Chieh Ho Tsa Chih* 14(7), 427-428.

Xu, R.H., X.E. Peng, G.Z. Chen and G.L. Chen, 1992. "Effects of *Cordyceps sinensis* on natural killer activity and colony formation of B16 melanoma" *Chinese Medical Journal* Feb; 105(2): 97-101.

Yamada, Y., H. Nanba, H. Kuroda, 1990. "Antitumor effect of orally administered extracts from fruitbody of *Grifola frondosa* (Maitake)."*Chemotherapy* (Tokyo) 38, 8: 790-796.

Yamaguchi, N., J. Yoshida, LJ Ren, et al., 1990. "Augmentation of various immune reactivities of tumor-bearing hosts with an extract of *Cordyceps sinensis.*" *Biotherapy* 2(3): 199-205.

Yamaguchi, Y., S. Kagoto, K. Nakamura, K. Shinozuka & M. Kunitomo, 2000. "Inhibitory effects of water extracts from fruiting bodies of cultured *Cordyceps sinensis* on raised serum lipid peroxide levels and aortic cholesterol deposition in atherosclerotic mice" *Phytotherapy Research* Dec; 14(8)650-652.

Yamamato, Y, H. Shirono, K. Kona, & Y. Ohashi, 1997. "Immunopotentiating activity of the water-soluble lignin rich fraction prepared from LEM—the extract of the solid culture medium of *Lentinus edodes* mycelia. *Bioscience. Biotechnology & Biochemistry* Nov.; 61(11):1909-12.

Yan, S.C., 1988. "Clinical and experimental research on *Polyporus umbellatus* polysaccharide in the treatment of chronic viral hepatitis" *Chung Kuo Chung Hsi I Chieh Ho Tsa Chih* Mar; 8(3) 141-3, 131.

Yang, D.A., 1991. "Inhibitory effect of Chinese herb medicine on urinary bladder cancer. An experimental and clinical study." *Chung-Hua-Wai-Ko-Tsa-Chih* Jun. 29(6): 393-5, 399.

Yang, D.A., S. Li, & X. Li, 1994. "Prophylactic effects of zhu-ling and BGG on postoperative recurrence of bladder cancer" *Chung-Hua-Wai-Ko-Tsa-Chih*, July: 32 (7) 433-4.

Yang et al., 1985. "Treatment of sexual hypofunction with *Cordyceps sinensis*" Jiangxi Zhongyiyao 5:46-47. From the *Abstracts of Chinese Medicines* 1: 401.

Yang, W., T. Hu, D. Win, 1992. "The experiments on the *Ganoderma lucidum* extract for its anti-aging and invigoration effects." *The 4th International Symposium on Ganoderma lucidum*. Seoul, Korea.

Yang, M.M., Z. Chen, J.S. Kwok, 1992. "The antitumor effect of a small polypeptide from *Coriolus versicolor* (SPCV)" *American Journal of Chinese Medicine* 20(3-4): 221-32.

Yang, Q.Y. & C.Y. Kwok, ed., 1993. *PSP International Symposium.* Shanghai: Fudan University Press.

Yang, Q.Y. & Wang, M., 1994. "The effect of *Ganoderma lucidum* extract against fatigue and endurance in the absence of oxygen". *Proceedings of Contributed Symposia 59 A,B. 5th International Congress.* Vancouver, Canada, August 14-21, 101-104.

Yang, Q.Y. & J.N. Fang, X.T. Yang, 1994. The isolation and identification of two polysaccharides of *Ganoderma lucidum* (GL-A, GL-B). *Proceedings of Contributed Symposium 59 A,B at the 5th International Mycological Congress,* Vancouver, Canada, August 14-21.

Yap, A.T. & M.L. Ng, 2002. "Lentinan as a possible 'oral vaccine' against tumor development" *Proceedings of the 7th International Mycological Congress Oslo* 11-17 August, pg. 54.

Yoshida, J. 1989. "Antitumor activity of an extract of *Cordyceps sinensis* (Berk.) Sacc. against murine tumor cell line." *Japan J. Exper. Med.* 59: 157-160.

You, J., D. Hau, K. Chen & H. Huang, 1994. "Combined effects of Chuling (*Polyporus umbellatus*) extract and mitomycin on experimental liver cancer" *American J. Chinese Med.* 22(1): 19-28.

Zang, M. & N. Kinjo, 1998. "Notes on the alpine Cordyceps of China and nearly nations" *Mycotaxon* LXVI: 215-229.

Zeng, Q., J. Zhao, and Z. Deng. 1994(?) "The Anti-tumor Activity of *Flammulina velutipes* Polysaccharide (FVP)." *Edible Fungi of China* vol. 10, no. 2.

Zhang, L. and M. Yu, 1993. "Influence of Ling Zhi on natural killer cells—Immunopharmacological study (5). From The research on *Ganoderma lucidum* (part one). Shanghai: Shanghai Medical University Press, 246-253.

Zhang L.X., H. Mong, X.B. Zhou, 1993. "Effect of Japanese Ganoderma lucidum (GL) planted in Japan on the production of interleukin-2 from murine splenocytes." *Chung Kuo Chung Hsi I Chieh Ho Tsa Chih* 13(10): 613-5.

Zhang, J., G. Wang, H. Li, C. Zhuang, T. Mizuno, H. Ito, H. Mayuzumi, H. Okamoto & J. Li, 1994. "Antitumor active protein-containing glycans from the Chinese mushroom Songshan Lingzhi, *Ganoderma tsuga*e mycelium" *Bioscience, Biotechnology & Biochemistry* 58:1202-1205.

Zhang, M.& N.Kinjo, 1998. "Notes on the Alpine Cordyceps of China and Nearby Nations" *Mycotaxon* 66: 215-219

Zhang, H., F. Gong, Y. Feng and C. Zhang, 1999. "Flammulin purified from the fruitbodies of *Flammulina velutipes* (Curt.:Fr.) Karst. *International Journal of Medicinal Mushrooms*, vol. 1, pp. 89-92.

Zhang, J., Q. Tang, M. Zimmerman-Kordmann, W. Reutter & H. Fan, 2002. "Activation of B lymphocytes by GLIS, a bioactive proteoglycan from *Ganoderma lucidum*" *Life Science* Jun 28;71(6)623-38.

Zhong, Y.H., Y.L. Liu & S.C. Yan, 1991. "Effect of *Polyporus umbellatus* polysaccharide on function of macrophages in the peritoneal cavities of mice with liver lesions" *Zhong Xi Yi Jie He Za Zhi* Apr 11:225-6, 198.

Zhou, A.R., 1987. "Studies on antitumor activity of Tremella polysaccharides." *J. Beijing Med. Univ.* 19: 150-.

Zhou, L., W. Yang, Y. Xu, Q. Zhu, Z. Ma, T. Zhu, X., Ge & J. Gao, 1990. "Short term curative effect of cultured *Cordyceps sinensis* (Berk.) Sacc. mycelia in chronic hepatitis B." *Chinese Journal of Materia Medica* 15: 53-55, 65.

Zhou, D.H. & L.Z. Lin, 1995. "Effect of Jinshubao capsule on the immunological function of 36 patients with advanced cancer" *Chung-Kuo-Chung-Hsi-I-Chieh-Ho-Tsa-Chih* Aug: 15(8) :476-8.

Zhou S. & Y. Gao, 2002. "The immunomodulating effects of *Ganoderma lucidum* (Curt.: Fr) P. Karst. (Ling Zhi, Reishi mushroom) Aphyllophoromycetideae). *International Journal of Medicinal Mushrooms* 4, 1: 1-12.

Zhu, D. 1987. "Recent advances on the active components in Chinese medicines" *Abstracts of Chinese Medicines* 1: 251-286.

Zhu, J.L. & C. Liu, 1992. "Modulating effects of extractum semen Persicae and cultivated Cordyceps hyphae on immuno-dysfunction of in-patients with post-hepatitic cirrhosis" *Zhongguo Zhong Xi Yi Jie Ha Za Zhi* April; 12(4):207-9, 195.

Zhu, J.S., G.M. Halpern, & K. Jones, 1998. "The scientific rediscovery of an ancient Chinese herbal medicine: *Cordyceps sinensis* Part I" *The Journal of Alternative and Complementary Medicine* vol. 4, no. 3, pp. 289-303.

Zhu, J.S., G.M. Halpern, & K. Jones, 1998. "The scientific rediscovery of an ancient Chinese herbal medicine: *Cordyceps sinensis* Part I" *The Journal of Alternative and Complementary Medicine* vol. 4, no. 4, pp. 429-457.

Zhu, M., Q. Chang, L.K. Wond. F.S. Chong & R.C. Li, 1999. "Triterpene antioxidants from *Ganoderma lucidum*" *Phytotherapy Research* 13, 529-531.

Zhu, H.S., X.L. Yang, L.B. Wang, D.X. Zhao & L. Chen, 2000. "Effects of extracts from sporoderm-broken spores of *Ganoderma lucidum* on HeLa cells" *Cell Biology & Toxicology* 16(3):201-6.

Zusman, I., R. Reifen, O. Livini, P. Smirnoff, P Gurevich, B. Sandler, A. Nyska, R. Gal, Y. Tendler & Z. Madar, 1997."Role of apoptosis, proliferating cell nuclear antigen and p53 protein in chemically induced colon cancer in rats fed corncob fiber treated with the fungus *Pleurotus ostreatus*" *Anticancer Research* May-June 17(3C):2105-13.

Noteworthy Popular Articles

Beinfield, H., 1997. "Medicinal mushrooms: help yourself to a serving of health." *Nature's Impact*, December.

Chilton, J. 1993. "What are the health benefits of mushrooms?" *Let's Live*, Dec., pp. 24-29.

Dharmananda, S., 1988. "Medicinal mushrooms." *Bestways Magazine*, July, pp. 54-58.

Hobbs, C., 1997. "Mushroom medicine" *Vegetarian Times*, Nov. pp. 96-98.

Hobbs, C., 1997. "Medicine mushrooms" *Herbs for Health*, pp. 52-53. Jan/Feb.

Jones, K., 1997. "An ancient Chinese secret promotes longevity and endurance." *Healthy & Natural Journal*, vol. 3, issue 3, pp. 90-93.

Jones, K., 1997. "Shiitake: medicine in a mushroom" *Herbs for Health*, pp. 48-50, 54. Jan/Feb.

Smith, C. 1994. "Gold medal herbs". *Natural Health* May/June, pp. 85-87

Smith, J. 2002. "Medicinal mushrooms: their therapeutic properties and current medical usage with special emphasis on cancer treatments." *Cancer Research UK*, August 2002.

Stamets, P., 2000. "Novel anti-viral compounds from mushrooms" *Herbalgram* 51: 24-27,

Stanislaus, C., 1996. "Ling zhi - medicine of kings." *New Editions Health World*, pp. 38-41.

Steinman, D., 1995. "Potent protectors." *Natural Health*, Nov-Dec. pp. 92-95; 134-135.

Weil, A. 1993. "Boost immunity with mushrooms." *Natural Health*, May-June, pp. 12-16.

Weil, A., 1997. "Miraculous mushrooms." *Dr. Andrew Weil's Self Healing Newsletter*, May, 1997.

Wiley, C. 1991. "The medicinal side of mushrooms." *Vegetarian Times*, March 1991.

Books on the Medicinal Properties of Mushrooms*

Halpern G.M., 1999. *Cordyceps: China's healing mushroom* Avery Publishing Group, Garden City Park, New York

Hobbs, C., 1995. *Medicinal Mushrooms: an Exploration of Tradition, Healing and Cultures.* Interweave Press.

Jones, K., 1997. *Cordyceps: Tonic Food of Ancient China.* Sylvan Press.

Jones, K., 1995. *Shiitake: The Healing Mushroom.* Healing Arts Press.

Mondoa, E. & M. Kitei, 2001 *Sugars that Heal: The New Healing Science of Glyconutrients* Ballantine Books, New York

Stamets, P. 1993, 2000. *Growing Gourmet & Medicinal Mushrooms.* Ten Speed Press.

Willard, T., 1995. *Reishi Mushroom: Herb of Spiritual Potency and Medical Wonder.* Sylvan Press.

Journals and Notable Proceedings
on the Medicinal Properties of Mushrooms

"*Ganoderma*: Systematics, Phytopathology and Pharmacology" ed. by P.K. Buchannan, R.S. Hseu, and J.M. Moncalvo. *Proceedings of Contributed Symposia 59,B 5th International Mycological Congress*, Vancouver, August 14-21, 1994.

"International Journal of Medicinal Mushrooms" ed. S.P.Wasser. Begell House, New York.

"Mushroom Biology and Mushroom Products" ed. by S.T. Chang, J.A. Buswell, and S. Chiu. *Proceedings of the First International Conference on Mushroom Biology and Mushroom Products*, August 23-26, 1993, The Chinese University of Hong Kong, Hong Kong.

"Mushroom Biology and Mushroom Products" ed. by D.J. Royse. *Proceedings of the Second International Conference*, University Park, Pennsylvania, June 9-12, 1996.

"Mushrooms: The Versatile Fungus-Food and Medicinal Properties" ed. by T. Mizuno in *Food Reviews International* vol. 11, no. 1., 1995. Marcel Dekker, Monticello, New York.

Finkbine, S., Odom, J., 2001 "Reversing Hepatitis C" *Alternative Medicine*, July, pp. 39-48.

O'Donnell, S.A., 1999. "Mushroom Medicine" *Prevention*, August, pp. 112-117.

Stamets, P., 2002. "Novel Antimicrobials from mushrooms" *Herbalgram*, 54: pp. 29-33.

Weil, A., 2002. "Splenda; Sjogren's; Help for HIV; and More" *Dr. Andrew Weil's Self Healing Newsletter*, May.

Weil, A., 2002. "7 Steps to Better Lungs" *Dr. Andrew Weil's Self Healing Newsletter*, June.

Weil, A., 2002. "Healing with Dr. Andrew Weil - Living proof: There is hope for beating cancer." *Prevention*, August, pp. 93-94.

Short Glossary

apoptosis: programmed cell death.

fruitbody: a mushroom, the fleshy, reproductive structure generated from the mycelium.

haptene: typically low molecular weight polysaccharides, which react *in vivo* with homologous antibodies.

host-mediated response (HMR): an activity of a host organism in response to an external stimulus.

immunomodulator: a substance that helps the immune system rebalance into a state of normal equilibrium.

immunostimulating: a substance that activates the immune system, resulting in a classic immune response, i.e. the production of lymphocytes, antibodies, etc.

interleukin lymphokines: polypeptides produced by lymphocytes, and activating dormant T cells, and stimulating other lymphocytes.

macrophages monocytes originating from lymphoid tissues, responding to foreign substances (i.e. bacteria) or cancerous cells, destroying them through phagocystosis or secretion of specific cytokines, such as tumor necrosis factors (TNF's).

mycelium, mycelia: the filamentous, threadlike network of microscopic fungal cells.

natural killer cells: non-B and non-T lymphocytes that bind to diseased cells and secrete cytotoxic compounds. NK cells are the first line of defense against the spread of tumors.

primordium, primordia: the youngest stage of mushroom formation, also known as 'pinheads' for their appearance.

sclerotium, sclerotia: an asexual, dormant stage of the mycelium characterized by densely packed, ball-like structures, often forming underground, in darkness, and typically surviving extending periods of time before regeneration into mycelium and/or fruitbodies.

tumor necrosis factor the causal factor, typically a protein, regulating the programmed death of tumor cells, activated, in many cases, by cytotokines.

Index

Agaricus blazei, 6, 13, 47, 49, 65
agarikon, 7, 20, 21
AIDS, 54
amadou, 18, 19
Aminoglycoside, 59
Anti-bacteria, 42, 52
Anti-inflammatory, 14, 21, 26, 27, 34, 38
Anti-viral, 10, 16, 25, 30, 33, 42, 43, 48, 52, 54, 56, 59, 71
apoptosis, 34, 37, 93
Arabinoxylane, 9,16, 28, 40, 44, 54, 71
arthritis, 19, 21, 26, 44
Asthma, 21, 25, 58, 59
Atherosclerosis, 26
Birch Polypore, 11, 12, 3
Black Forest Mushroom, 51
Black Hoof, 34
breast cancer, *(Grifola frondosa, Lentinula edodes, Trametes versicolor)* 14, 17, 30, 44, 49, 65, 67,68
bronchitis, 25
cancer, 5, 6, 8, 9, 14, 17, 19, 25, 26, 27, 29, 30, 31, 33-36, 38, 40-44, 46, 48-52, 54, 56, 58, 59, 63-69, 71
Candida, 10, 28, 54, 69, 72
Caterpillar Fungus, 57
cervical/uterine cancer *(Agaricus blazei, Inonotus obliquus, Inonotus obliquus, Phellinus linteus Schizophyllum commune, Trametes versicolor)* 17, 19, 25, 33, 40, 41, 43, 48, 71
Chaga, 16, 32, 34
chemoprotective, 16
Chemotherapy, 31, 35, 38, 40, 42, 67
Cholesterol, 14, 25, 48, 50, 52, 55, 56, 58, 69
Chorei, 38
Choreimaitake, 38
Chongcao, 57
chronic fatigue syndrome (CFS), 15, 28, 54
Chu Ling, 38
Cinder Conk, 32
Clinker Polypore, 32
Collybia velutipes (see *Flammulina velutipes*) 13, 50
colorectal cancer: *(Agaricus blazei, Grifola frondosa, Phellinus linteus)* 17
Cordyceps sinensis, 6, 13, 14, 15, 16, 17, 30, 57, 58, 59, 60, 61, 65, 72
Coriolus versicolor (see *Trametes versicolor*), 10, 13, 42, 43
Diabetes, 15, 31, 72
Diuretic, 23, 38, 39
Dong Chong Xia Cao, 6, 57
Enokidake, 50
Enokitake, 6, 50
ergosterol, 8, 18, 33, 35, 42, 44, 45, 47, 48, 52, 71
Flammulina velutipes, 6, 13, 14, 17, 44, 50, 51, 52
Free radical, 15, 26, 27, 29, 43, 65, 70
free radical scavenging, 15, 29
Ganoderma lucidum, 6, 8, 10, 13, 15, 16, 17, 24-29, 69
gastric/stomach cancer *Hericium erinaceus, Phellinus linteus, Schizophyllum commune, Trametes versicolor)*, 17, 19, 35, 40, 42, 46
gastritis, 46
Golden Needle Mushroom, 50
Grifola frondosa, 8, 13, 14, 15, 17, 29, 31
Grifola umbellata (see *Polyporus umbellatus*), 13, 38
grifolan, 30-32
heavy metals, 39, 65
Hen-of-the-Woods, 29
Hepatitis, 16, 27, 38-39, 59
Hericium erinaceus, 6, 10, 13, 17, 45-46, 69
Himematsutake, 6, 47
Hiratake, 55
Host-mediated response, 10, 48, 52, 93
Houtou, 45
human immunodeficiency virus (HIV) 16, 26-28, 30, 33, 43, 54, 56
hypoglycemic, 33
inflammation, 14, 26, 37, 58, 70
Inonotus obliquus, 16, 17, 32
Jin Zhen Gu, 50
Kabanoanatake, 32
Kanbatake, 36
Kawaratake, 42

Kawariharatake, 47
Kumotake, 29
lead, 60, 72
Leukemia *(Cordyceps sinensis, Ganoderma lucidum Grifola frondosa, Polyporus umbellatus,*
    Trametes versicolor) 17, 26, 39, 43, 58
LEM, 52, 54
lentinan, 10, 52-54
Lentinula edodes, 6, 10, 14, 16, 17, 44, 51, 53-54
leukemia, 17, 26, 39, 43, 58
Lion's Mane, 45
liver, 6, 16, 17, 27, 30, 31, 34, 38, 39, 52, 56, 59, 62, 69, 71
liver cancer *(Ganoderma lucidum Grifola frondosa, Lentinula edodes, Phellinus linteus, Polyporus*
    umbellatus, Trametes versicolor) 17
lung cancer *(Cordyceps sinensis, Ganoderma lucidum, Grifola frondosa, Polyporus umbellatus,*
    Trametes versicolor) 17, 30, 31, 34, 38, 39, 71
lymphocytes, 25, 27, 35, 43, 50, 52, 68
lymphoma *(Cordyceps sinensis, Flammulina velutipes)* 17, 50
Maitake, 6, 8, 15, 29-32, 67-68
Malaria, 10, 22, 38-39
Mannentake, 24
Melanoma *(Lentinula edodes, Phellinus linteus, Piptoporus betulinus*
    Polyporus frondosus (see *Grifola frondosa))* 17, 37
Meshima/Mesima, 6, 34-36
Meshimakobu, 34
Monkey's Head, 45
Mushikusa, 29
nephrotoxicity, 59
nitric oxide, 26-27, 31, 48, 71
Organic, 32, 65-66
Oyster Mushroom, 55-56
Parasites, 10, 37
Phellinus linteus, 17, 34-36
Piptoporus betulinus, 12, 17
Platelet, 14
Pleurotus ostreatus, 6, 14, 16, 17
Polyporus umbellatus, 6, 10, 16, 17, 36
Prostate, 17, 26, 30, 31
prostate cancer *(Flammulina velutipes, Ganoderma lucidum, Grifola frondosa, Lentinula edodes)*
    17, 30, 31, 43, 50
PSK, 42-44
PSP, 42-43
Radiation therapy, 16, 38, 41, 43, 67
radioprotective, 16
Rheumatoid arthritis, 44
RNA, 47, 52, 56
Royal Sun Agaricus, 47
Sarcoma *(Agaricus blazei, Ganoderma lucidum, Pleurotus ostreatus)* 8, 17, 35, 39, 43-44, 50, 56, 65
Salmonella, 48
Sangwhang, 34
Schizophyllum commune, 16, 17, 40, 54
septic shock, 54
Sex, sexuality, 21, 41, 58
Shiitake, 6, 10, 16, 29, 32, 42, 44-45, 47, 51-54, 70
skin, 28, 29
Songrong, 47
spleen, 26-27, 43, 58
Split Gill Polypore, 40-41, 67, 70
Suehirotake, 16, 40, 67, 70
Trametes versicolor, 6, 8, 16, 17, 18, 42-44, 54
Tochukaso, 57
Tomogitake, 55
triterpenes, 8, 23-24, 33
triterpenoids, 8, 20, 23, 25-27, 33, 37, 71
Turkey Tail, 9, 16, 42, 34
tumor necrosis factors, 25-27, 31, 48, 65, 93
Umbrella Polypore, 38
Urinary tract infection, 39
Xiang Gu, 51
Yamabushitake, 6, 45
Yertsa Gonbu, 57
Yun Zhi, 6, 8, 9, 42-43, 67
Zhu Ling, 6,10, 16, 38-39, 67

Photo/Illustration Credits

Page 9—Drawing of an argillite plate, carved by Charles Edenshaw in approx. 1890. Redrawn from a photograph, courtesy of the Field Museum of Natural History,Chicago, with permission of Robert Blanchette.
Page 12—Photo by Solomon Wasser
Page 29—Photo by Taylor Lockwood
Page 38—Photo by David Bill
Page 40—Photo by Tom Volk (www.TomVolkFungi.net)
Page 45—Photo by Taylor Lockwood
Page 57—Photo by Taylor Lockwood

Other Books by the Author

Growing Gourmet & Medicinal Mushrooms
The Mushroom Cultivator (co-author)
Psilocybin Mushrooms of the World
Psilocybe Mushrooms and their Allies
Gardening with Gourmet & Medicinal Mushrooms (in preparation/press)

Dusty Wu Yao collecting mushrooms in the Old Growth forests in the Elwa River drainage of the Olympic Rainforest, Washington State.